RIA RIVERA

DR. SEBI'S ALKALINE & ANTI-INFLAMMATORY DIET FOR BEGINNERS

The Authentic Detox Recipes to Minimize Inflammation and Improve Your Way of Living Thanks to Sebi's Lifelong Health Lifestyle

30-Day Meal Plan

About this Book

From A-list celebrity clients like Jon Travolta and Michael Jackson to honorable song mentions by rap legends, Dr. Sebi is known for his novice approach to diet. The Dr. Sebi diet is a revolutionary concept that seeks to rejuvenate, cleanse and restore the health of your body.

In this book, you will learn about what was the philosophy behind this diet and its benefits. 160 recipes with meal plans and a shopping list are a step-by-step guide that will prove necessary for any beginner. This is why special care was taken to ensure it is easy to understand for everyone.

3 Short Easy Steps to Ensure Success

1. Start with the **7-DAY DETOX MEAL PLAN** and **10-DETOX DRINKS.** All toxins from your body will be removed! *(Available for free for a limited period! – Download your free copy below with QR-Code!)*

2. Use the **SHOPPING LIST** to buy grocery items that are permissible in Dr. Sebi's diet. *(Available for free for a limited period! – Download your free copy below with QR-Code!)*

3. Use meal plans to meal prep for the month. A **30-DAY MEAL PLAN** will help you in this regard. It is custom designed with all the alkaline plant-based ingredients. Every recipe is unique and delicious so you enjoy this journey every step of the way.

GET YOUR FREE BOOK BONUSES NOW!

(DOWNLOAD FOR FREE WITH THE BELOW INSTRUCTION!)

Do you want to unlock complete knowledge about how to detox your body with this fantastic diet?

- Are you interested to discover 10 detox drinks?

- Are you curious about the 7-day detox meal plan?

- Would you have access to a detailed shopping list?

SCAN THE QR CODE BELOW AND UNLOCK THE FULL POTENTIAL OF DR.SEBI DIET!

DR. SEBI
Bonuses
Full Body Detox

Bonus 1) 7 Day Detox Meal Plan
Bonus 2) 10 Detox Drinks
Bonus 3) Detailed Shopping List

FREE BONUS!

INSTRUCTION ON HOW TO UNLOCK YOUR FREE BONUSES

Only 2 simple steps to unlock your free bonuses:

1.   **Scan the QR code (paperback version) or click the hyperlink (Kindle version)** on the previous page and unlock full knowledge of Dr. Sebi's diet. Start now to detox your body!

2.   **Let me know how you are excited about all the contents!** I look forward to your opinion on the book and the bonus content!

SCAN THE QR CODE BELOW AND LEAVE A QUICK REVIEW ON AMAZON TO SHARE YOUR THOUGHTS ON THIS BOOK.

The best way to do it? Simple! **You can upload a brief video** *with your thoughts. I will greatly appreciate an honest opinion about the book!*

Don't you want to create a video? Don't worry! **You can do a short review with some photos** *of dishes made thanks to this book or take photos of the most beautiful parts of the book.*

NOTE: You don't have to feel obligated, but it would be highly appreciated!

Table of Contents

Introduction

Who Is Dr. Sebi?

As humanity has progressed, unfortunately, we have drifted far away from natural life and natural food. Toxicities have been made into our homes through various ready-to-eat and processed food items. The harm that these items do is not visible to the naked eye in the short term but soon enough consumption over a large time leaves devastating effects. From high blood pressure to obesity and heart disease, these effects have long-lasting effects on our health and quality of life.

Born in Honduras a young mind, Alfredo Bowman recognized this issue quite well. Better known as Dr. Sebi, he like many men and women had asthma, diabetes, and impotency. Western medicine failed to treat his ailments. This was one of the reasons why he could understand the plight of people because he too was once in their shoes. It was only after he visited Mexico that an herbalist there treated him. There he discovered the true power of herbs and natural unprocessed food. He took wisdom to form the places he went and the cultures he visited.

He later immigrated to the US and started his practice. Many people were drawn to his truth, his love, his knowledge, and his dietary regime. His clients included many Hollywood a-list celebrities and influential rappers. Over 30 years of his knowledge was amalgamated in the form of, "Dr. Sebi's Cell Food."

The philosophy behind this is quite simple. Our body should be optimally in a state of homeostasis, anything that upsets this natural harmony is a threat to our body and health. So, what causes this imbalance? The elements that might cause this are what we eat. This is why Dr. Sebi curated a list of food items that he considered to be not allowed. This list includes animal and fish products (the rest will be discussed later in this chapter in tabular form).

If we talk about the science behind this, we even find evidence from the science of the existence of microplastic in fish and shellfish. This plastic is so tiny that our human eye is incapable of even visualizing it. Consumption of plastic that can't deteriorate may lead to harmful health effects. Not only this animal products also have growth hormones and antibiotics that become a part of our body when we consumes them.

The blood running through our veins is at slightly alkaline ph. 7.4 This is why alkaline food will help our body heal and function optimally. So, how can we help our cells to repair themselves? It is through Dr. Sebi's diet. The essence of the Earth is to heal.

"Let thy medicine be thy food."

Author's Journey

For as far back as I can recall I have been "the fat kid." I hated picture day and would do anything to just avoid looking at myself in the mirror. As I hit 19, acne just made all of this worse. What I failed to recognize at that age was that many issues that I had were aggravated by the kind of food I ate. I loved chicken wings and a good hamburger. I had made terrible food choices and those choices had their fangs deep into my self-image. Food for some people becomes a source of comfort and a harmful relationship thus forms. Fighting against this can be an emotionally and physically grueling task. I stumbled upon Dr. Sebi's diet on the internet and I decided to try my best to follow it.

I wrote the foods not allowed in my diary and made sure to bring them with me every time I shopped. For the first time in many years, I had to face the demons that lived in my head. I was able to feel courageous enough to commit. After a week on it, I could see and feel the results. My skin was glowing and I dropped 2.5 pounds by the end of the first week. I felt energized and motivated. As the month's end drew nearer, I could feel myself change. Never had I been so amazed and grateful.

This diet gives you a perspective on life and helps you to listen to your body. If my body is telling me I am full then I listened and saved the leftovers for the next meal. I also felt I got fuller faster and stayed fuller longer. I stopped overeating funnily enough after a month of cutting out sugar entirely, I didn't fancy sweets. Somehow, I felt they were too sweet for my liking. These behavior modifications are possible. Even though many told me I was too far gone, one person gave me hope and so I wrote this book to share this hope with you.

The legacy of Dr. Sebi lives on. DR. Sebi was a pioneer. Even though Dr. Sebi passed away in 2014, the legacy of Dr. Sebi is carried on by his daughter and grandchildren. What drew in the hearts of the common ordinary people and celebrities? It was DR. Sebi's nature to be non-judgmental toward others. His vast knowledge did not make him egotistical and boastful.

As a humble soul, he reached his hand to others to spread knowledge through love rather than hatred. The power of his love for the betterment of people gave him the courage to fight for his people to start a healthier diet.

I believe in you; you have got this. Whether this diet is to fight health issues, weight issues, or weak immunity, you can do it! To assist you I will share with you what I know best, cooking. My recipes will help you enjoy this journey. So, when you decide to improve your diet, you don't have to sacrifice your favorite kind of pasta or dessert. I have curated these recipes with alternative ingredients that are permissible in Dr. Sebi's diet. 160 recipes with meal plans and a shopping list will aid you every step of the way.

Good luck!

What Should We Eat?

When it comes to the type of food, we should eat on the Dr. Sebi diet.

- ***Natural Water***

Instead of sodas and energy drinks, we should drink water. Water is a part of all of our cells and dehydration is often unnoticed by many people. This leads to headaches and less than-optimal function. Water helps us to excrete the toxic products in our urine safely and water also acts as a protective pillow for organs like our brain. Even the human baby is protected by it the mother's womb.

- ***Alkaline Non-Cross-Pollinating Plants***

Plants that do not cross-pollinate are permissible in this diet. These alkaline plants are rich in phytochemicals and antioxidants that cleanse any harmful chemicals in our bodies. Phytochemicals help our bodies to fight against viral bacterial and fungal infections. Phytochemicals are widely used in medicine to treat and manage symptoms of diseases like Alzheimer's and age-related eye diseases.

- ***Gluten Intolerance and Lactose Insufficiency***

If you can't tolerate gluten-containing food items or if you are lactose intolerant then you do not have to worry at all as this diet is perfect for you. You can enjoy a lot of delicious kinds of pasta and snacks that are not containing gluten in them. This diet will also help you to maintain the homeostasis of your body thus relieving all the symptoms that come with these ailments.

- ***Protein Sources***

The protein sources in Dr. Sebi's diet are of great importance. Tofu, hemp seeds, and walnuts

are excellent sources of plant-based protein. These protein sources do not have cholesterol and your carbon footprint with these sources is so much less compared to animal protein. These plant-based proteins help our body to shift towards homeostasis and heal itself.

What Should We Avoid Eating?

- ### *Meat And Fish*

Meat and fish are not permissible in Dr. Sebi's diet. Dr. Sebi recalled all of his ailments had not returned once he began an alkaline plant-based diet. He went through it this is why he was aware of how hard it is and how magnificent the change can feel when you have to courage to conquer your inherent biases.

- ### *Hybrid Plants*

Hybrid plants are those that are crossbred from two different varieties of plants to obtain a plant with positive characteristics of both varieties. The fact of the matter is that these hybrid plants are not naturally occurring in the environment. Humans intervene and carry out cross-pollination and that leads to hybridization. Hence, the Dr. Sebi diet promotes the consumption of non-hybrid alkaline plants.

- ### *The Verdict on Microwaving Food*

Do not use microwaves to cook or heat food. Microwaving food does not make it radioactive. But we have to keep in mind that food is often wrapped in some packaging. When we heat it, the phthalates will go from the packaging into the food. This will lead to the consumption of these compounds without the human eye or nose even noticing it. Moreover, a lot of research is needed to access how much these foreign chemicals affect the human body. An increase in the diagnosis of cancer and auto-immune conditions in the past decades may be linked to it. Phthalates are often linked with breast cancer, developmental issues, and even asthma and impotency.

Food Allowed and
Food Not Allowed

FOOD ALLOWED

YES!

VEGETABLES

WILD ARUGULA	GARBANZO BEANS
BELL PEPPERS	TURNIP GREENS
SQUASH	KALE
CUCUMBER	LETTUCE
CHICKPEAS	MUSHROOMS
WATERCRESS	ZUCCHINI

FRUITS

CANTALOUPE	ELDER BERRRY
APPLE	PEARS
LIME	TOMATO
BANANA	PLUMS
MELON	CURRANTS
ORANGE	COCONUT

FOOD ALLOWED

YES!

RASPBERRY	AVOCADO
PAPAYA	TAMARIND
MANGO	PEACHES

NUTS

BRAZIL NUTS	WALNUTS

SEEDS

HEMP SEEDS	SESAME SEEDS
RAW SESAME TAHINI BUTTER	

OIL

OLIVE OIL	GRAPE SEED OIL
COCONUT OIL	HEMP SEED OIL
AVOCADO OIL	SESAME SEED OIL

SPICES

CAYENNE PEPPER	TARRAGON
BASIL	DILL
BAY LEAF	OREGANO
CLOVE	ONION POWDER
SALT	THYME
SAGE	GINGER

SWEETS

AGAVE SYRUP	WILD RICE

FOOD ALLOWED

YES!

DATE SUGAR	RYE
GRAINS	FONIO
QUINOA	SPELT
TEF	
ALL HERBAL TEAS ARE ALLOWED	

FOOD NOT ALLOWED

NO!

VEGETABLES

STRING BEANS	SPINACH
JICAMA	ASPARAGUS
ICEBERG	SHITAKE
MUSTARD GREENS	

NUTS

RAW ALMONDS	ALMOND BUTTER
HAZEL NUTS	PINE NUTS

SPICES

CORIANDER	CILANTRO
CUMIN	PARSLEY
ALL SPICES	LEMON GRASS

SWEETS

MAPLE SYRUP	MAPLE SUGAR

30-Day
Meal Plan

	BREAKFAST	*LUNCH*	*DINNER*
MONDAY	Banana Spelt Pancakes	Banana and Strawberry Smoothie	Black Olives and Tomatoes Wrap
TUESDAY	Detox Green Smoothie	Cheesy Chickpea Pasta	Quinoa Bread Sandwich With Coconut Cheese and Arugula
WEDNESDAY	Green Apple Smoothie	Mushroom Stuffed Wraps with Tahini Butter	Fruit Salad with Dandelion Greens
THURSDAY	Teff Porridge	Blueberry Coconut Milkshake	Arugula And Sesame Wrap Seasoned with Achiote
FRIDAY	Alkaline Vegetable Omelet	Pesto Pasta	Alkaline Sloppy Garbanzo Beans
SATURDAY	Spelt Bread French Toast	Papaya And Figs Smoothie in Walnut Milk	Roasted Red Pepper Curry
SUNDAY	Alkaline Banana Milkshake	Coconut Butter Sandwich with Tahini Sesame Butter	Wakame Seaweed Wraps

	BREAKFAST	**LUNCH**	**DINNER**
MONDAY	Green Apple Smoothie	Tofu Marinara Pasta	Turnip and Zucchini Wraps
TUESDAY	Strawberries Smoothie Bowl	Stuffed Bell Peppers	Alkaline Mushroom Stew
WEDNESDAY	Sweet Amaranth Recipe	Papaya and Figs Smoothie In Walnut Milk	Fruit Salad with Dandelion Greens
THURSDAY	Blueberries and Hemp Smoothie Bowl	Kamut Patties	Quinoa Bread Sandwich With Coconut Cheese and Arugula
FRIDAY	Alkaline Quiche	Bell Pepper Pasta with Kale	Alkaline Chili Stew
SATURDAY	Baked Apple Slices	Herb and Apple Green Juice	Black Currants and Pear Salad
SUNDAY	Waffles with Mushrooms	Vegetable Fajita	Grilled Zucchini Wrap

	BREAKFAST	**LUNCH**	**DINNER**
MONDAY	Berry and Peach Smoothie	Coconut Cheese Pasta	Fruit Salad with Dandelion Greens
TUESDAY	Sweet Amaranth Recipe	Peach and Mango Juice	Alkaline Chickpea Salad
WEDNESDAY	Kamut Cereal	Strawberry Muffins	Fried Wild Rice
THURSDAY	Alkaline Banana Milkshake	Watermelon and Coconut Water Juice	Cucumber and Onion Salad With Hempseed Oil
FRIDAY	Peach and Apple Smoothie	Mushroom Zucchini Pasta	Vegan Pizza Boats
SATURDAY	Spelt Bread French Toast	Avocado and Dates Smoothie	Alkaline Meatballs
SUNDAY	Blueberries Muffin	Chickpea Burger	Cherry Tomato and Okra Salad
MONDAY	Creamy Hemp Heart Porridge	Herb and Apple Green Juice	Grilled Zucchini Wrap

	BREAKFAST	LUNCH	DINNER
MONDAY	Apple and Quinoa Breakfast	Chickpea Spaghetti	Guacamole Salad
TUESDAY	Kamut Cereal	Banana and Strawberry Smoothie	Avocado Pizza Topped with Mushrooms
WEDNESDAY	Alkaline French Toast	White Chickpea Sandwich with Tomatillo	Boiled Mushrooms and Roasted Bell Peppers
THURSDAY	Banana Spelt Pancakes	Papaya and Figs Smoothie In Walnut Milk	Turnip and Zucchini Wraps
FRIDAY	Banana Spelt Pancakes	Vegan Pizza Boats	Squash and Walnuts Salad
SATURDAY	Teff Porridge	Peach and Mango Juice	Fruit Salad with Dandelion Greens
SUNDAY	Creamy Hemp Heart Porridge	Trumpet Mushroom Sandwich	Vegetable and Mushrooms Stew
MONDAY	Alkaline Quiche	Avocado and Dates Smoothie	Cucumber and Onion Salad with Hempseed Oil

Chapter-1
Breakfast

Banana Spelt Pancakes

Prep Time
11 minutes

Cook Time
11 minutes

Yield
8/9

What you will need

- **Spelt flour**, 1 cup /8 oz. /227g
- **Bananas**, small, 3, mashed
- **Coconut milk**, ¾ cup /177ml
- **Hempseed oil**, 2 tablespoons /30ml
- **Agave syrup (100% pure)**, 2 tablespoons /30ml

Directions

1. Mix the hempseed oil, agave syrup, and bananas. Now add spelt flour in it and add milk and stir it continuously to attain the desired consistency.

2. Heat the skillet and lightly oil it with hemp seed oil, then transfer the batter into the small circles and let the pancakes cook properly, 5 minutes on each of its sides.

3. Serve warm and enjoy!

Nutritional Content

Calories 129kcal | **Crabs** 16g | **Protein** 5g | **Fat** 5.7g | **Fiber** 1.2g

Green Apple Smoothie

Prep Time
6 minutes

Cook Time
0 minutes

Yield
1

What you will need

- **Green apple**, 1 large
- **Ice cubes**, 6
- **Coconut milk**, ½ cup /118ml
- **Sea moss**, ½ teaspoon /2.5g
- **Dates**, 4

Directions

1. Firstly, chunk the apple, and discard the seed from the dates.

2. Then put all the ingredients in the processor and blend them till it is smooth.

3. Put it into the glass and serve.

Nutritional Content

Calories 172.6kcal | **Crabs** 34g | **Protein** 1.2g | **Fat** 2.7g | **Fiber** 6g

Alkaline Vegetable Omelet

Prep Time
5 minutes

Cook Time
7 minutes

Yield
1

What you will need

- **Abaza bean flour**, ¼ cup /2 oz. /56.7g
- **Spring water**, 1/3 cup /79ml
- **Plum tomato**, 1 tablespoon /14g
- **Brazil nut cheese**, 1 tablespoon /14g
- **Basil**, ¼ teaspoon /1.25g
- **Mushrooms**, chopped, 1 tablespoon /14g
- **Onion powder**, ¼ teaspoon /1.25g
- **Cayenne**, ¼ teaspoon /1.25g
- **Oregano**, ¼ teaspoon /1.25g
  - **Onion**, chopped, 1 tablespoon /14g
    - **Sesame oil**, 1 teaspoon /5ml
    - **Sea salt**, one pinch

Directions

1. In a bowl include, Abaza bean flour and water then add all spices in it and stir it till it is going to be very thin almost like a batter

2. In a pan warm, the sesame oil then includes all the vegetables and a pinch of salt, and sauté it then pour the batter over the vegetables and let it cook for 3 minutes so it can be flipped easily then flip it and cook for 5 minutes more.

3. You can add a tablespoon of Brazil nut cheese and fold it so that it looks like an omelet.

4. Serve warm.

Nutritional Content

Calories 137.8kcal | **Crabs** 12.3g | **Protein** 5.5g | **Fat** 6.1g | **Fiber** 2.8g

Spelt Bread French Toast

Prep Time
4 minutes

Cook Time
9 minutes

Yield
6

What you will need

- **Hemp milk**, ¾ cup /177ml
- **Spelt bread**, 6 slices
- **Cloves**, grounded, ½ teaspoon /2.5g
- **Sea salt**, one pinch
- **Grapeseed oil**
- **Ginger powder**, one pinch
- **Sliced strawberries**, a few slices
- **Spring water**, ¼ cup /59ml
- **Garbanzo bean flour**, ½ cup /4 oz. /113.4g
- **Agave syrup**, 2 tablespoons/30ml

Directions

1. Mix all the ingredients in a bowl and beat it till blended well.

2. Now put this batter in the long container and soak bread in it for 8 minutes or more, changing sides halfway through.

3. Now heat the skillet put grapeseed oil and put slices on it and cook 3 minutes per side till brown.

4. Place on the plate and top with strawberry slices and serve.

5. Enjoy the peanut butter toast with a side of egg.

Nutritional Content (piece)

Calories 87kcal | **Crabs** 12.8g | **Protein** 2.5g | **Fat** 2.08g | **Fiber** 1.86g

Sweet Amaranth Recipe

Prep Time
6 minutes

Cook Time
24 minutes

Yield
4

What you will need

- **Amaranth**, 1 cup /8 oz. /227g
- **Hempseed milk**, 1/3 cup /79ml
- **Spring water**, 3 cups /750ml
- **Raw agave**, 2 tablespoon /28g
- **Clove**, one pinch
- **Sea salt**, 1 teaspoon /5g
- **Ginger**, ¼ teaspoon /1.25g

Directions

1. Take a saucepan and include amaranth, water, and sea salt in it. Place it on heat and mix the ingredients for a minute. Let it boil.

2. Now add hempseed milk, cover it and cook for 14 minutes or more. Include ginger, clove, and agave and stir to blend them.

3. Let it cook for 5 to 6 minutes more till it attains a porridge-like consistency. You can add sea moss at this step.

4. Pour in the bowl and enjoy!

Nutritional Content

Calories 288.6kcal | **Crabs** 41.6g | **Protein** 10.3g | **Fat** 7.2g | **Fiber** 6.2g

Alkaline Banana Milkshake

Prep Time
6 minutes

Cook Time
0 minutes

Yield
1

What you will need

- **Bananas**, 2 small
- **Hemp milk**, 1 cup /250ml
- **Cloves**, grounded, 1 teaspoon /5g
- **Agave syrup**, 1 teaspoon /5g

Directions

1. Firstly, take a blender then include bananas, hemp milk, cloves, and agave syrup in the blender and blend it till its consistency is smooth.

2. Put it into the serving glass and serve.

Nutritional Content

Calories 227.8kcal | **Crabs** 46g | **Protein** 4.3g | **Fat** 7g | **Fiber** 8.2g

Berry and Peach Smoothie

Prep Time
10 minutes

Cook Time
0 minutes

Yield
2

What you will need

- **Peaches**, frozen ½ cup /4 oz. /113.4g
- **Blueberries**, frozen ½ cup /4 oz. /113.4g
- **Strawberries**, frozen ½ cup /4 oz. /113.4g
- **Cherries**, frozen ½ cup /4 oz. /113.4g
- **Agave syrup**, 1 tablespoon /14g
- **Sea moss gel**, 1 tablespoon /14g
- **Coconut Water**, 1 cup/250ml
- **Hemp seeds**, 1 tablespoon, /14g

Directions

1. In the blender include all the ingredients and let it blend for 1 minute or more till smooth.

2. If it is too thick add coconut water about ¼ cup and blend for 20 seconds more.

3. Enjoy!

Nutritional Content

Calories 163.2kcal | **Crabs** 27.4g | **Protein** 3.5g | **Fat** 3.25g | **Fiber** 5.5g

Detox Green Smoothie

 Prep Time 10 minutes

 Cook Time 0 minutes

 Yield 2

What you will need

- **Dandelion greens**, 1 large bunch
- **Blueberries**, ½ cup /4 oz. /113.4g
- **6 dates**
- **Bananas**, 3 baby
- **Watercress**, 1 handful
- **Ginger**, 1 thumb
- **Lime juice**, ¼ cup /59ml
- **Burdock root powder**, 1 tablespoon /14g
- **Coconut water**, 2 cups /500ml

Directions

1. In the blender include all the ingredients and blend for 1 minute or more till it is blended into a thick drink.

2. You can either serve it immediately or store it in the refrigerator for chilling.

Nutritional Content

Calories 312kcal | **Crabs** 67g | **Protein** 6.6g | **Fat** 1.5g | **Fiber** 10.35g

Blueberries Muffin

 Prep Time 10 minutes

 Cook Time 30 minutes

 Yield 8

What you will need

- **Hemp milk**, 1 cup /250ml
- **Teff flour**, ¾ cup/6 oz. /170g
- **Grapeseed Oil**, 1 teaspoon /5g
- **Blueberries**, ½ cup /4 oz. /113.4g
- **Kamut flour**, ¾ cup /6 oz. /170g
- **Sea Moss Gel**, ¼ cup /2 oz. /56.7g
- **Sea Salt**, ½ teaspoon /2.5g
- **Agave syrup**, 1/3 cup /79ml

Directions

1. Warm the oven before to 400 °F (200 °C). In the bowl combine the flour, milk, sea moss gel(optional), sea salt, and agave syrup till combined or blended well, then include blueberries in it.

2. Grease the muffin pan with grapeseed oil, and put the muffin batter in it.

3. Let it bake for 25 to 30 minutes.

4. Serve and enjoy!

Nutritional Content (1 muffin)

Calories 144.7kcal | **Crabs** 26.8g | **Protein** 3.7g | **Fat** 1.93g | **Fiber** 2.97g

Teff Porridge

| **Prep Time** | **Cook Time** | **Yield** |
| 5 minutes | 17 minutes | 2 |

What you will need

- **Teff grain**, ½ cup /4 oz. /113.4g
- **Sea salt**, one pinch
- **2 walnuts halves**, for topping
- **Agave (optional)**, 1 teaspoon /5g
- **Spring Water**, 2 cups /500ml

Directions

1. In a pan bring the boil to the spring water. Add a pinch of sea salt.
2. Include Teff grain slowly in it while mixing.
3. Now place the lid over it and allow it to cook for 16 minutes or more.
4. Put it in the bowl top it with walnuts and serve.

Nutritional Content

Calories 86.9kcal | **Crabs** 13.95g | **Protein** 2.5g | **Fat** 2.6g | **Fiber** 1.5g

Kamut Cereal

| **Prep Time** | **Cook Time** | **Yield** |
| 5 minutes | 10 minutes | 2 |

What you will need

- **Kamut**, 2 cups /454g
- **Sea salt**, two pinches
- **Oregano**, 1 teaspoon/5g
- **Spring Water**, 4 cups /1000ml
- **Cayenne**, grounded, 1 teaspoon/5g
- **Onion powder**, one pinch

Directions

1. In a pan bring the boil to the spring water. Add a pinch of sea salt.
2. In the blender put Kamut and blend it till it looks like sand. Include it in the boiling water and mix it continuously. You can add more spring water to attain the consistency of your own choice.
3. Add the seasonings in it and stir it thoroughly. Serve.

Nutritional Content

Calories 233.4kcal | **Crabs** 41g | **Protein** 10g | **Fat** 1.6g | **Fiber** 7.9g

Apple and Quinoa Breakfast

Prep Time
5 minutes

Cook Time
16 minutes

Yield
1

What you will need

- **Apple**, grated, 1
- **Dates**, 2
- **Quinoa**, ½ cup /4 oz. /113.4g

Directions

1. Boil the water in the pan including the quinoa and cook for 15 minutes.

2. Then include grated apples and cook for 30 seconds more.

3. Ladle into the bowl and top it with dates.

Nutritional Content

Calories 223.6kcal | **Crabs** 43g | **Protein** 4.9g | **Fat** 2.1g | **Fiber** 6.7g

Peach and Apple Smoothie

Prep Time
5 minutes

Cook Time
0 minutes

Yield
1

What you will need

- **Apple**, sliced, 1
- **Organic peach**, 1
- **Agave syrup**, 1 tablespoon /15ml
- **Seville orange**, juiced, 1
- **Walnut milk (homemade)**, 1 cup /250 ml

Directions

1. Include all the ingredients in the processor and process it till it has a smoothie-like texture.

2. Your yummy smoothie is ready to serve.

Nutritional Content

Calories 395.6kcal | **Crabs** 64g | **Protein** 4.9g | **Fat** 11.8g | **Fiber** 6.3g

Strawberries Smoothie Bowl

Prep Time
6 minutes

Cook Time
0 minutes

Yield
1

What you will need

- **Walnut milk**, ¼ cup /59ml

- **Strawberries**, frozen, 1 cup /8 oz. /227g

- **Hemp hearts**, 1 tablespoon /14g

- **Agave syrup**, 1 tablespoon /15ml

- **Banana**, frozen, 1

- **Raspberries and strawberries**, for topping, ¼ cup /2 oz. /56.7g

Directions

1. Include the walnut milk, strawberries, and agave syrup into the blender and blend, till it has a smooth consistency.

2. Pour into a bowl and top with your blueberries, strawberries, and hemp seeds, and enjoy

Nutritional Content

Calories 382kcal | **Crabs** 58g | **Protein** 7.6g | **Fat** 10g | **Fiber** 10g

Alkaline French Toast

Prep Time
7 minutes

Cook Time
10 minutes

Yield
7

What you will need

- **Coconut milk**, 1 cup /250ml

- **Date sugar**, 1 teaspoon /5g

- **Spelt bread (thick sliced)**, 7 slices

- **Agave syrup**, 2 teaspoons /30ml

- **Chickpea flour**, ¼ cup /4 oz. /56.7g

- **Grapeseed oil**, 3 tablespoons /45ml

Directions

1. Stir the coconut milk, date sugar, and chickpea flour in a wide shallow bowl.

2. Drizzle grapeseed oil into a pan. Before dipping the bread stir the batter again. Now dip each side of bread in the batter and soak for seconds, then transfer the slice of bread to the pan.

3. Cook for 2 minutes on each of its sides, till it is light brown. You can add more oil as required in between the bread slices.

4. Serve with agave syrup and fresh fruit of your own choice.

Nutritional Content

Calories 188kcal | **Crabs** 23.4g | **Protein** 8.4g | **Fat** 14g | **Fiber** 4.25g

Baked Apple Slices

Prep Time
10 minutes

Cook Time
25 minutes

Yield
4

What you will need

- **Apples**, cored, sliced, 6 large
- **Agave syrup**, ½ cup /125ml
- **Date sugar**, 1 tablespoon /14g
- **Walnuts**, ½ cup /4 oz. /113.4g
- **Avocado oil**, 4 tablespoons /60ml
- **Cloves**, grounded, 1 teaspoon /5g

Directions

1. Warm the oven before to 350 °F (180 °C).

2. Combine the agave syrup, cloves, avocado oil, and date sugar in oven friendly baking dish or pan. Mix them well.

3. Now put sliced apples in the pan and mix well to coat with the mixture.

4. Cook for 25 minutes by placing it in the center of the oven, till soft.

5. Serve with sprinkled walnuts.

Nutritional Content

Calories 525kcal | **Crabs** 72g | **Protein** 3g | **Fat** 24g | **Fiber** 9.3g

Creamy Hemp Heart Porridge

Prep Time
8 minutes

Cook Time
15 minutes

Yield
4

What you will need

- **Walnut milk (homemade)**,
  1 ½ cup /375ml

- **Amaranth flour**,
  ¼ cup + 2 tablespoons /84.7g

- **1 banana**, mashed

- **Unsweetened shredded coconut**,
  ¼ cup + 2 tablespoons /84.7g

- **Hemp hearts**, 2/3 cup /151g

- **Sea salt**, one pinch

- **Agave syrup**, to taste

- **Brazil nuts**, 6 nuts

Directions

1. Firstly, boil the walnut milk, then include amaranth flour, sea salt, mashed banana, and hemp hearts in it.

2. Lower the heat to let it simmer and mix it till it is thick.

3. Include agave syrup according to your taste.

4. Serve in bowls topped with Brazil nuts.

Nutritional Content

Calories 460.7kcal | **Crabs** 16.05g | **Protein** 16.3g | **Fat** 32g | **Fiber** 6.15g

Waffles With Mushrooms

 Prep Time
15 minutes

 Cook Time
26 minutes

 Yield
4

What you will need

WAFFLES
- **Spelt flour**, 2 cups/16 oz. /454 g
- **Hemp Milk**, 1 cup /250ml
- **Spring water**, 1 cup /250ml
- **Agave syrup**, ¼ cup /59ml
- **Grapeseed oil**, 3 tablespoons/45ml
- **Sea Moss gel (optional)**, 2 teaspoon /10g

MUSHROOMS
- **Oyster mushrooms**, 1 to 2 bunches
- **Waffle batter**, ¾ cup /177ml
- **Basil**, grounded, 1 teaspoon /5g
- **Garbanzo bean flour**, ¾ cup /6 oz. /170g
- **Sea salt**, ½ teaspoon /2.5g and Onion powder, 2 teaspoon /10g
- **Cayenne powder**, ½ teaspoon /2.5g
- **Oregano**, 1 teaspoon /5g and a dash of salt

Directions

1. Mix flour and seasonings or the crust then include ¼ cup water and make a dough Include waffle ingredients and half a cup water in a bowl and whisk it till combined well. If it is too thick then you can add more water.

2. Grease the waffle maker with grapeseed soil and cook waffles using waffle maker instructions. Keep ¾ cup of batter aside.

3. Now include garbanzo bean flour and half of all the seasonings in a bowl and mix mushrooms in it then add the remaining seasoning to the waffle batter, thin it with water, and coat mushrooms.

4. Heat the oil in the skillet and cook the mushroom for 6 minutes, changing sides after halftime. Now top the waffles with mushrooms

Nutritional Content

Calories 454kcal | **Crabs** 61.4g | **Protein** 13.9g | **Fat** 14.5g | **Fiber** 9.6g

Blueberries and Hemp Smoothie Bowl

 Prep Time
6 minutes

 Cook Time
0 minutes

 Yield
1

What you will need

- **Walnut milk (homemade)**, ¾ cup /177ml
- **Burro bananas**, frozen, 2
- **Date sugar**, 2 tablespoons /28g
- **Hemp seeds**, 2 tablespoons /28g
- **Wild blueberries**, frozen, ¾ cup /168g

Directions

1. Include the ingredients mentioned above into the blender and keep blending it, till it has a smooth consistency.

2. Ladle it into a bowl and top it with your favorite toppings and enjoy

Nutritional Content

Calories 530kcal | **Crabs** 71g | **Protein** 11.6g | **Fat** 19.5g | **Fiber** 12.8g

Alkaline Quiche

Prep Time
15 minutes

Cook Time
55/65 minutes

Yield
4/6

What you will need

FOR CRUST

- **Spelt flour**, 1 cup /8 oz. /227g
- **Sea salt**, 1 teaspoon /5g
- **Basil**, 1 teaspoon /5g
- **Spring water**, 1 cup /250ml
- **Onion powder**, 1 teaspoon /5g
-

FILLING

- **Garbanzo bean flour**, 1 cup/8 oz. /227g
- **Kale**, chopped, 1 cup/8 oz. /227g
- **Hemp milk**, ¾ cup /177ml
- **Red and white onions**, chopped, ½ cup /4 oz. /113.4g
- **Red**, green, or yellow pepper, chopped, ½ cup /4 oz. /113.4g
- **Onion powder**, 1 tablespoon /14g
- **Mushrooms**, chopped, ½ cup /4 oz. /113.4g
- **Basil**, 1 teaspoon /5g
- **Cayenne powder**, ¼ teaspoon /1.25g
- **Oregano**, 1 teaspoon /5g
- **Sea salt**, one pinch
- **Leftover water from cooked chickpeas**, ¾ cup /177ml
- **Brazil nut cheese**, 1 cup /8 oz. /227g
- **Alkaline garlic sauce**, 1 tablespoon /14g

Directions

1. Mix flour and seasonings or the crust then include ¼ cup water and make the dough you can add more water if it is too wet.

2. Place the dough on the surface with flour and roll it out to the size of the pan. Grease the pan lightly with grapeseed oil and place dough in it and trim off the corners or edges.

3. Now for the preparation of the quiche mixture include bean flour, garlic sauce, seasonings, milk, and leftover chickpea water in the blender and blend it till it is combined well.

4. Warm the oven before to 350 ˚F (180 ˚C). Combine the onions, pepper, kale, and mushrooms in a bowl.

5. Now add the vegetables to the pie pan, top with Brazil nut cheese and add the quiche mixture. Cover with foil to prevent the crust from getting hard, and cook for 55 to 65 minutes. And make sure that 10 minutes before the completion of cooking time remove the foil.

6. Let it cool for some time then cut it and serve.

Nutritional Content

Calories 159kcal | **Crabs** 21g | **Protein** 7.78g | **Fat** 2.6g | **Fiber** 5.58g

Chapter-2
Side Dishes

Fruits Salad

Prep Time
15 minutes

Cook Time
15 minutes

Yield
3

What you will need

- **Spelt pasta**, 1 cup/3oz./85g
- **Cherry tomatoes (chopped)**, ½ cup/3oz./90g
- **Sea salt**, ½ teaspoon/0.11oz./3g
- **Strawberries (halve)**, 1 cup/5.3oz./152g
- **Apple**, ½ cup/2.2oz./62g
- **Grapes**, ½ cup/2.6oz./75g
- **Peach**, 1 /5oz./150g

Directions

1. Boil the spelt pasta for 15 minutes at medium flame, until it becomes soft.

2. Meanwhile cut the fruits; apples, and peaches into slices. Cut the strawberries into halves.

3. When the pasta is done, drain it for 5 minutes. Add pasta to a fruit bowl. Add salt to it. Mix all the items well.

4. Now divide them into 2 bowls, and top them with cherry tomatoes. Serve and enjoy!

Nutritional Content

Calories 169.3kcal | **Carbs** 38.3g | **Protein** 5g | **Fat** 0.9g | **Fiber** 3.8g

Savory Watermelon

Prep Time
15 minutes

Cook Time
0 minutes

Yield
4

What you will need

- **6 olives sliced**, 24g
- **Basil leaves**, 1 teaspoon, 1g
- **Watermelon slice**, 145g
- **Vegan cheese**, 1tablespoon, 15g
- **Tomato puree**, 2 teaspoons, 10g

Directions

1. Cut the watermelon slice in a triangular shape, like the pizza triangle

2. Arrange watermelon triangular slices in a circular pan and put feta cheese and olives on it. Top it with tomato puree.

3. Sprinkle basil leaves and serve.

Nutritional Content

Calories 125kcal | **Crabs** 18g | **Protein** 1.6g | **Fat** 6g | **Fiber** 1.5g

Creamy Coconut Green Salad

Prep Time
10 minutes

Cook Time
0 minutes

Yield
4

What you will need

- **Coconut cream**, ¼ cup/2 oz. /61g
- **Dill**, 1 cup/0.3oz./8.9g
- **Green olives**, 1 cup/4.76oz./135g
- **Lettuce**, 1 cup/1.66oz./47g
- **Dandelion greens**, 1 cup/2oz./55g
- **Cucumber**, 1 cup/4oz./119g
- **Coconut oil**, 1 tablespoon/0.5oz./13.6g

Directions

1. Add sliced green olives, chopped lettuce, dill, dandelion greens, and cucumber in a large bowl.

2. Toss with coconut oil.

3. Dish out and serve salad, topped with coconut cream.

Nutritional Content

Calories 122.3kcal | **Carbs** 7.9g | **Protein** 1.8g | **Fat** 10g | **Fiber** 2.2g

Zucchini and Wild Rice

Prep Time
15 minutes

Cook Time
20 minutes

Yield
3

What you will need

- **Zucchini**, 1 cup/5.2oz./148g
- **Wild rice (boiled)**, 1 cup/5.78oz./164g
- **Tomato**, 1/2 cup/3oz./90g
- **Onions**, ½ cup/3.4oz./97g
- **Cayenne pepper**, 2 teaspoons/0.06oz./1.8g
- **Avocado oil**, 1 tablespoon/0.5fl.oz./13.6ml

Directions

1. Cut the onion, tomatoes, and zucchini and sautéed those in avocado oil for 6 minutes.

2. Add boiled wild rice to sautéed vegetables.

3. Stir rice and vegetables properly.

4. Sprinkle cayenne pepper and sea salt over it.

5. Remove from heat. Serve and enjoy!

Nutritional Content

Calories 124kcal | **Carbs** 17.7g | **Protein** 3.5g | **Fat** 5.1g | **Fiber** 2.5g

Coconut Cheese Creamy Mushrooms

Prep Time
12 minutes

Cook Time
13 minutes

Yield
4

What you will need

- **Coconut cheese**, ½ cup/2oz./60g
- **Mushrooms**, 2 cups/6.7oz./192g
- **Sage (chopped)**, 2 teaspoons/0.05oz./1.3g
- **Sea salt**, 1 teaspoon/0.21oz./6g
- **Sesame oil**, 2 tablespoons/1fl. Oz. /27ml
- **Basil leaves (chopped)**,
  1 tablespoon/0.09oz./2.7g
- **Habanero**, 0.18oz./5g
- **Coconut cream**, ¼ cup/2oz./61g

Directions

1. Firstly, boil the walnut milk, then include amaranth flour, sea salt, mashed banana, and hemp hearts in it.

2. Lower the heat to let it simmer and mix it till it is thick.

3. Include agave syrup according to your taste.

4. Serve in bowls topped with Brazil nuts.

Nutritional Content

Calories 159kcal | **Carbs** 5.9g | **Protein** 5.7g
Fat 13.3g | **Fiber** 0.7g

Blueberry Quinoa

Prep Time
10 minutes

Cook Time
18 minutes

Yield
4

What you will need

- **Quinoa**, 1 cup/6oz./170g
- **Blueberry**, 1 cup/5oz./148g
- **Sesame seeds**, 1 tablespoon/0.3oz./9g
- **Coconut milk**, ½ cup/4fl.oz./120ml
- **Agave syrup**, 1 tablespoon/0.74fl. oz./21ml

Directions

1. Boil the quinoa in salty water. Reduce the flame and boil it at low flame for 15 minutes.

2. Meanwhile, add some blueberries and agave syrup in a blender and blend them. Set them aside.

3. When quinoa is done, dish it out. Top it with blueberry paste and fresh blueberries.

4. Serve with sprinkled sesame seeds and enjoy!

Nutritional Content

Calories 212kcal| **Carbs** 37.3g| **Protein** 6.7g| **Fat** 4.4g| **Fiber** 4.2g

Sliced Tomatoes with Coconut Cheese

Prep Time
5 minutes

Cook Time
0 minutes

Yield
2

What you will need

- **Tomatoes (sliced)**, 1 cup/6.35oz./180g
- **Coconut cheese**, ½ cup/1oz./30g
- **Basil**, 2 tablespoon/0.75oz./21.2g
- **Avocado oil**, 1 tablespoon/0.5fl.oz./13.6ml

Directions

1. Cut the tomato into slices, and drizzle avocado oil over it.

2. Put cubed coconut cheese over it.

3. Serve with sprinkled fresh basil leaves and enjoy!

Nutritional Content

Calories 133.9kcal| **Carbs** 3.8g| **Protein** 4.6g| **Fat** 12.1g| **Fiber** 1.2g

Garbanzo Beans with Black Olives

Prep Time
15 minutes

Cook Time
40 minutes

Yield
3

What you will need

- **Black olives**, ½ cup/2.83oz./80.2g
- **Garbanzo beans**, 1 cup/5.7oz./164g
- **Onion chopped**, ½ cup/3.4oz./97g
- **Tomatoes chopped**, ½ cup/3oz./90g
- **Cucumber**, 1 cup/4.2oz./119g
- **Fresh basil leaves**, ¼ cup/0.37oz./10.6g

Directions

1. Soak the beans for 6 hours, and boil them at low medium flame for 40 minutes.

2. Meanwhile, add chopped onion, tomatoes, and cucumber in a bowl, and add black olives over it.

3. When beans become soft, remove them from heat and dish them out. Allow them to cool at room temperature.

4. Now mix beans in a black olive bowl, and sprinkle chopped basil over it. Serve and enjoy!

Nutritional Content

Calories 143.8kcal | **Carbs** 21.7g | **Protein** 6g | **Fat** 4.5g | **Fiber** 5.7g

Roasted Kale

Prep Time
5 minutes

Cook Time
3 minutes

Yield
2

What you will need

- **Kale**, 1 cup/0.74oz/21g
- **Sesame seeds oil**, 2 tablespoons/1 fl. oz./27.3ml
- **Cayenne pepper**, 1 teaspoon/0.06oz./1.8g

Directions

1. Heat sesame oil in a saucepan. Add kale to it and stir fry for 2 minutes, until it is wilted.

2. When the kale is roasted, remove it from the heat.

3. Serve with sprinkled cayenne pepper and enjoy!

Nutritional Content

Calories 126.9kcal | **Carbs** 1g | **Protein** 0.4g | **Fat** 13.9g | **Fiber** 0.7g

Baked Okra in Avocado Oil

Prep Time
10 minutes

Cook Time
15 minutes

Yield
2

What you will need

- **Okra**, 1 cup/3.5oz./100g
- **Habanero**, 1 /0.18oz./5g
- **Avocado oil**, 2 tablespoons
- **Sea salt**, ½ teaspoon/0.11oz./3g

Nutritional Content

Calories 212kcal | **Carbs** 37.3g | **Protein** 6.7g | **Fat** 4.4g | **Fiber** 4.2g

Directions

1. Wash the okra and pat dry it. Remove the stems and cut the okra into 1 inch's slices.

2. Coat the baking sheet with avocado oil.

3. Toss the okra with crushed habanero, and place this spiced okra on a baking sheet

4. Sprinkle salt over it. Bake it for 15 minutes in preheated oven at 450 °F or 232 °C

5. When okra becomes brown and soft, remove from oven.

6. Serve and enjoy!

Baked Zucchini

Prep Time
12 minutes

Cook Time
12 minutes

Yield
3

What you will need

- **Zucchini**, 1 cup/5.24oz./148.5g
- **Grape seed oil**, 2 tablespoons/1fl. Oz./27.3ml
- **Brazil nuts**, 1 tablespoon/0.29oz./8.3g
- **Achiote seasoning**, 1 teaspoon/0.05oz./1.5g

Nutritional Content

Calories 108.2kcal | **Carbs** 2.2g | **Protein** 1g | **Fat** 11.1g | **Fiber** 0.7g

Directions

1. Peel off the zucchini and cut them into slices.

2. Coat the baking paper with grape seed oil.

3. Place the oil and artichoke seasoning tossed zucchini on the baking paper.

4. Place them in the oven at 350 °F or 176.6 °C and bake them for 12 minutes.

5. When zucchini become light green color and soft, remove it from the oven.

6. Sprinkle chopped Brazil nuts over it. Serve and enjoy!

Baked Asparagus

Prep Time
9 minutes

Cook Time
15 minutes

Yield
2

What you will need

- **Asparagus**, 1 cup/4.7oz./134g
- **Cayenne pepper**, 2 teaspoons/0.12oz./3.5g
- **Sesame oil**, 2 tablespoons/1fl.oz./13.6ml
- **Sea salt**, ½ teaspoon/0.11oz./3g

Directions

1. Wash the asparagus, and trim its ends. Season it with cayenne pepper and salt.

2. Brush the parchment paper with sesame oil. Place seasoned asparagus in the oven.

3. Bake it for 15 minutes at 425 °F or 220 °C. When it becomes light brown from the side, remove it from the oven.

4. Serve with tomato sauce and enjoy!

Nutritional Content

Calories 139.5kcal | **Carbs** 3.6g | **Protein** 1.7g | **Fat** 14g | **Fiber** 1.9g

Baked Mushrooms with Wild Arugula

Prep Time
8 minutes

Cook Time
20 minutes

Yield
2

What you will need

- **1 cup mushrooms/3.39oz./96g**
- **Avocado oil**, 1 tablespoon/0.5fl. oz./13.6ml
- **Wild arugula**, 1 cup/0.71oz./20g
- **Onion powder**, 1 teaspoon/0.08oz./2.3g
- **Thyme**, 1 teaspoon/0.03oz./0.9g
- **Sage**, 1 teaspoon/0.01oz./0.3g

Directions

1. Peel of mushrooms, wash them, and dry them.

2. Add mushrooms, thyme, sage, onion powder, and wild arugula in a bowl. Mix all items properly.

3. Now coat baking paper with avocado oil. Bake seasoned mushrooms for 20 minutes at 400 °F or 204 °C.

4. When mushrooms become dark color and fork tender. Remove them from the oven. Serve and enjoy!

Nutritional Content

Calories 78.9kcal | **Carbs** 3.2g | **Protein** 1.9g | **Fat** 7.1g | **Fiber** 1g

Tomato Salsa

Prep Time
8 minutes

Cook Time
0 minutes

Yield
2

What you will need

- **Tomatoes (chopped)**, 1 cup/6.35oz./180g
- **Onion (chopped)**, ½ cup/3oz./97g
- **Lime**, 2 tablespoons/1fl.oz./30ml
- **Sage**, 1 tablespoon/0.03oz./0.9g
- **Basil leaves**, 1 tablespoon/0.05oz/1.5g

Directions

1. Add chopped tomatoes and onions to a bowl. Add sage and basil to it.

2. Add lime juice and toss vegetables with lime properly.

3. Place it in the refrigerator before serving.

4. Serve with pasta or mushrooms and enjoy!

Nutritional Content

Calories 41kcal | **Carbs** 9.6g | **Protein** 1.5g | **Fat** 0.3g | **Fiber** 2g

Thyme-Roasted Butternut Squash

Prep Time
5 minutes

Cook Time
30 minutes

Yield
3

What you will need

- **Butternut squash**, 1 cup/7oz./205g
- **Avocado oil**, 1 tablespoon/0.5fl.oz./13.6ml
- **Onion powder**, 1 teaspoon/0.08oz./2.3g
- **Thyme**, 1 tablespoon/0.08oz./2.4g
- **Habanero**, 1 /0.18oz./5g

Nutritional Content

Calories 72.6kcal | **Carbs** 8g |
Protein 0.7g | **Fat** 4.6g | **Fiber** 2.4g

Directions

1. Peel off the butternut squash and cut them into cubes.

2. Now crush the habanero and apply it to the cubed butternut. Now season butternut cubes with thyme and onion powder.

3. Place the seasoned butternut squash on baking paper coated with oil.

4. Bake butternut at 350 °F or 175 °C for 30 minutes.

5. When it becomes fork tender, remove them from the oven.

6. Serve with sprinkled thyme and enjoy! Serve and enjoy!

Baked Avocado Stuffed with Amaranth Greens

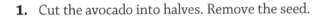

Prep Time
9 minutes

Cook Time
12 minutes

Yield
4

What you will need

- **Avocado**, 1 /4.8oz./136g
- **Amaranth greens**, 1 cup/1oz./28g
- **Tomatoes**, ½ cup/3oz./90g
- **Lettuce**, ½ cup/0.83oz./23.5g
- **Dandelion greens**, 1 cup/2oz./55g
- **Achiote seasoning**, 2 teaspoons/0.11oz./3g

Directions

1. Cut the avocado into halves. Remove the seed.

2. Fill the pit with amaranth green, tomatoes, lettuce, and dandelion green. Season all with achiote seasoning.

3. Now place the avocado halves filled with vegetables in the oven. Bake it for 12 minutes at 400 °F or 200 °C.

4. When the avocado is done, remove it from the oven. Serve and enjoy!

Nutritional Content

Calories 71.5kcal | **Carbs** 6.1g | **Protein** 1.5g | **Fat** 5.4g | **Fiber** 3.5g

Roasted Creamy Olives

Prep Time
6 minutes

Cook Time
10 minutes

Yield
2

What you will need

- **Olives**, 1 cup/4.76oz./135g
- **Coconut cream**, ¼ cup/2oz./61g
- **Avocado oil**, 1 tablespoon/0.5fl. oz./13.6ml

Directions

1. Cut the olives into slices. Place olive slices on the baking paper coated with avocado oil.

2. Bake olives for 10 minutes at 400 °F or 204 °C, until they become soft.

3. Now remove olives from the oven.

4. Top the olives with coconut cream. Serve and enjoy!

Nutritional Content

Calories 219.8kcal | **Carbs** 10.9g | **Protein** 2g | **Fat** 19.8g | **Fiber** 2.3g

Habanero Spiced Bell Peppers

 Prep Time
5 minutes

 Cook Time
6 minutes

 Yield
2

What you will need

- **Green bell pepper**, 1 cup/3.25oz./92g
- **Habanero**, 2 /0.35oz./10g
- **Onion powder**, 1 teaspoon/0.08oz./2.3g
- **Thyme**, 1 teaspoon/0.03oz./0.9g
- **Oregano**, 1 teaspoon/0.04oz./1g
- **Grape seed oil**, 1 tablespoon/0.5fl. oz./13.6ml

Directions

1. Heat grape seed oil in a pan, add chopped bell pepper to it and stir fry it for 2 minutes.

2. Now add crushed habanero pepper to it, and fry it for another 2 minutes. Continue stirring and add thyme, onion powder, and oregano to it.

3. Continue frying at low flame, until the bell pepper becomes soft.

4. Now remove from heat. Serve and enjoy!

Nutritional Content

Calories 80.9kcal | **Carbs** 3.7g | **Protein** 0.6g | **Fat** 7g | **Fiber** 1.3g

Deep-Fried Onion Rings

 Prep Time
14 minutes

 Cook Time
18 minutes

 Yield
5

What you will need

- **Butternut squash**, 1 cup/7oz./205g
- **Avocado oil**, 1 tablespoon/0.5fl.oz./13.6ml
- **Onion powder**, 1 teaspoon/0.08oz./2.3g
- **Thyme**, 1 tablespoon/0.08oz./2.4g
- **Habanero**, 1 /0.18oz./5g

Nutritional Content

Calories 134.2kcal | **Carbs** 8.3g | **Protein** 1.4g | **Fat** 11.1g | **Fiber** 1.3g

Directions

1. Cut the onion into the ring form. Heat the avocado oil in the saucepan.

2. Meanwhile, add spelt flour, salt, and onion powder to the bowl. Mix them well

3. Add ring onion to flour mixture, coat it properly and put to oil for deep frying.

4. After 4 minutes flip over to be fried from another side as well.

5. Now when the onion ring is fried, take it out, and pat it with tissue paper.

6. Serve with tomato sauce and thyme. Enjoy!

Butternut Squash Fries

Prep Time
10 minutes

Cook Time
40 minutes

Yield
2

What you will need

- **Butternut squash (sliced)**, 2 cups/9.5oz./268g

- **Sesame oil**, 2 tablespoons/1fl.oz./27ml

- **Sea salt**, ¼ teaspoon/0.05oz./1.5g

Nutritional Content

Calories 174.2kcal | **Carbs** 14.1g | **Protein** 1.2g | **Fat** 13.7g | **Fiber** 4.3g

Directions

1. Peel off the butternut squash and cut them into French fries shapes.

2. Preheat the oven to 425°F or 218.3°C.

3. Brush the parchment paper with sesame oil. Bake the fries for 40 minutes at the same temperature.

4. After 20 minutes interval flip over the fries.

5. Remove fries when they turn brown.

6. Serve with tomato sauce and enjoy!

Garbanzo Beans with Cayenne Pepper

Prep Time
8 minutes

Cook Time
45 minutes

Yield
2

What you will need

- **Garbanzo beans**, 1 cup/5.78oz./164g

- **Cayenne pepper**, 2 teaspoons/0.12oz./3.5g

- **Sea salt**, ¼ teaspoon/0.05oz./1.5g

Nutritional Content

Calories 219.8kcal | **Carbs** 10.9g | **Protein** 2g | **Fat** 19.8g | **Fiber** 2.3g

Directions

1. Soak the beans for 7 hours. After boiling bring them to a boil in salty water.

2. Boil them at medium flame for 45 minutes.

3. When beans are soft, remove them from heat and allow them to cool at room temperature.

4. Now pour in small bowls, and top with cayenne pepper and salt.

5. Serve and enjoy!

Zucchini fries

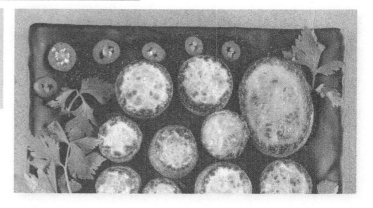

Prep Time
8 minutes

Cook Time
20 minutes

Yield
3

What you will need

- **Zucchini (sliced)**, 1 cup/5.2oz./148g
- **Avocado oil**, ¼ cup/2fl.oz./54.5ml

Nutritional Content

Calories 169kcal | **Carbs** 1.5g | **Protein** 0.6g | **Fat** 18.3g | **Fiber** 0.5g

Directions

1. Peep off the zucchini and cut them into slices.

2. Coat the baking paper with avocado oil. Place zucchini slices over it.

3. Bake for 20 minutes at 425 °F or 220 °C. Flip it over after 10 minutes.

4. When the zucchini color turns brown, remove it from the oven.

5. Serve with tahini sauce and enjoy!

Fire Roast Herbed Tomatoes

Prep Time
5 minutes

Cook Time
6 minutes

Yield
2

What you will need

- **Tomatoes**, 1 cup/6.35oz./180g
- **Dill**, 1 cup/0.31oz./8.9g
- **Thyme**, ½ cup/0.68oz./19.2g
- **Purslane**, ½ cup/0.76oz./21.5
- **Sesame oil**,
  2 tablespoons. /1 fl. Oz. /27.3ml

Nutritional Content

Calories 150.4kcal | **Carbs** 6.5g | **Protein** 1.7g | **Fat** 14.1g | **Fiber** 2.6g

Directions

1. Heat the sesame oil. Add tomatoes to it. Roast the tomatoes.

2. Add dill, sage, thyme, and Purslane. Stir fry all the ingredients for 5 minutes. Until all are roasted well.

3. Dish it out and serve!

Roasted Amaranth Greens with Coconut Cheese

Prep Time
2 minutes

Cook Time
5 minutes

Yield
2

What you will need

- **Amaranth green**, 1 cup/0.99oz./28g

- **Coconut cheese**, 1 tablespoon/1oz./30g

- **Sesame oil**, 2 tablespoons. /1 fl. Oz. /27.3m

Nutritional Content

Calories 178.5kcal | **Carbs** 0.6g | **Protein** 3.8g | **Fat** 18.7g | **Fiber** 0.6g

Directions

1. Fry the amaranth greens in sesame oil. Continue to fry, until it becomes wilted.

2. Now add coconut cheese to it, and keep siring until the cheese melts.

3. Remove from heat. Dish it out.

4. Serve and enjoy!

Chapter-3
Sandwiches, Pizzas, and Wraps

Quick Pizza

Prep Time
25 minutes

Cook Time
7 minutes

Yield
3

What you will need

- **Date sugar**, 1 teaspoon/0.11oz./3g
- **Sesame seeds**, 1 tablespoon/0.3oz./9g
- **Spelt flour**, 2 cups/8.5oz./240g
- **Sesame oil**, ¼ cup/2fl. Oz. /55g
- **Yellow bell pepper**, ½ cup/2.6oz./75g
- **Tomatoes (chopped)**, ½ cup/3oz./90g
- **Mushrooms**, ½ cup/2.8oz./78g
- **Onion (chopped)**, ½ cup/3.4oz./97.1g
- **Dates (chopped)**, 3 /0.14 cup/0.75oz./21.3g

Directions

1. Add sesame seeds, spelt flour, salt, and date sugar in a bowl, and mix all well. Add warm water to knead the dough.

2. Add sesame oil and knead the dough with soft hands, until it becomes smooth. Set it aside for 10 minutes. Now use a rolling pin to flatten the dough. Press the edges with your fingers.

3. Place it on the baking sheet and bake the crust for 7 minutes at 401⁰F or 205 ⁰C. When the crust becomes crisp, remove it from the oven.

4. Now top it with chopped tomato, onion, bell pepper, dates, and mushrooms. Cut it into 3 slices and serve.

Nutritional Content

Calories 504kcal | **Crabs** 70.2g | **Protein** 13.8g | **Fat** 21.9g | **Fiber** 11.3g

Pizza Topped with Arugula

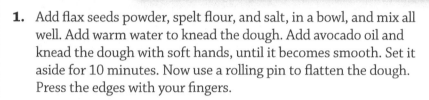

Prep Time	**Cook Time**	**Yield**
20 minutes	15 minutes	5

What you will need

- **Flax seeds powder**, 1 teaspoon/0.18oz./5g
- **Spelt flour**, 3 cups/13oz./360g
- **Avocado oil**, ¼ cup/2fl. Oz. /55g
- **Salt**, ½ teaspoon/0.11oz./3g
- **Arugula**, 8 leaves/0.56oz./16g
- **Tomatoes (chopped)**, 1 cup/6oz./180g
- **Coconut shredded**, 1.4oz./40g
- **Oregano**, 1 teaspoon/0.04oz./1g
- **Onion powder**, 1 teaspoon/0.08/2.3g
- **Tomato sauce**, 3 tablespoons/1.6oz/46g

Directions

1. Add flax seeds powder, spelt flour, and salt, in a bowl, and mix all well. Add warm water to knead the dough. Add avocado oil and knead the dough with soft hands, until it becomes smooth. Set it aside for 10 minutes. Now use a rolling pin to flatten the dough. Press the edges with your fingers.

2. Coat the baking sheet with avocado oil and place it on the baking sheet and bake the crust for 10 minutes at 401°F or 205 °C. When the crust becomes crisp, remove it from the oven. Now top it with tomato sauce, onion powder, oregano, and chopped tomato, and bake for another 5 minutes at 401°F or 205 °C.

3. Remove from oven, and sprinkle coconut powder and arugula. Serve and enjoy!

Nutritional Content

Calories 409kcal | **Crabs** 55g | **Protein** 11.8g | **Fat** 18.3g | **Fiber** 10g

Avocado Pizza Topped with Mushrooms

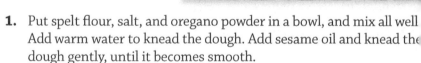
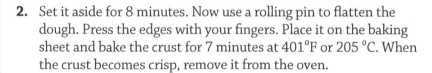

Prep Time	**Cook Time**	**Yield**
22 minutes	12 minutes	4

What you will need

- **Spelt flour**, 4 cups/12.7oz./360g
- **Sesame oil**, ¼ cup/2fl. Oz. /55g
- **Tomatoes (chopped)**, ½ cup/3oz./90g
- **Mushrooms**, ½ cup/2.8oz./78g
- **Avocado**, 6 slices/3oz./90g
- **Green bell pepper (chopped)**, ½ cup/2.6oz./75g
- **Onion powder**, 1 teaspoon/0.08oz./2.3g
- **Oregano**, 1 teaspoon/0.06oz./1.8g
- **Basil**, ½ teaspoon/0.02oz./0.7g
- **Plant butter**, 1 tablespoon/0.5oz./14g

Directions

1. Put spelt flour, salt, and oregano powder in a bowl, and mix all well. Add warm water to knead the dough. Add sesame oil and knead the dough gently, until it becomes smooth.

2. Set it aside for 8 minutes. Now use a rolling pin to flatten the dough. Press the edges with your fingers. Place it on the baking sheet and bake the crust for 7 minutes at 401°F or 205 °C. When the crust becomes crisp, remove it from the oven.

3. Now top it with chopped tomato, onion powder, bell pepper, basil, mushrooms, and avocado slices, and add the remaining sesame oil. Bake it for another 4 minutes, until vegetables become soft.

4. Remove from the oven. Top with plant butter and serve.

Nutritional Content

Calories 494kcal | **Crabs** 68.7g | **Protein** 14.5g | **Fat** 21.1g | **Fiber** 12.5

Black Olive Pizza

Prep Time	**Cook Time**	**Yield**
10 minutes	40 minutes	2

What you will need

- **Olives**, 1 cup/5.6oz./160g
- **Sesame seeds**, 1 tablespoon/0.3oz./9g
- **Spelt flour**, 2 cups/8oz./240g
- **Olive oil**, 2 tablespoons/1oz./27ml
- **Green bell pepper**, ½ cup/2.6oz./75g
- **Tomatoes (chopped)**, ½ cup/3oz./90g
- **Onion (sliced)**, ½ cup/1.7oz./48.5g
- **Vegan cheese (shredded)**, ¼ cup/50g

Directions

1. Knead a pizza dough using spelt flour and warm water splashes. Set it aside for 10 minutes. Now use a rolling pin to flatten the dough. Press the edges with your fingers.

2. Brush the baking sheet with olive oil and place the dough on it. Bake it for 7 minutes at 401°F or 205 °C. When the crust becomes crisp, remove it from the oven.

3. Now add chopped tomato, onion slices, and bell pepper, cheese, and bake for 5 minutes at the same temperature. Now remove it from heat and top it with sesame seeds and green olives. Serve and enjoy!

Nutritional Content

Calories 467kcal | **Crabs** 64.1g | **Protein** 13.7g | **Fat** 20.8g | **Fiber** 12.2g

Okra Topped Pizza

Prep Time	**Cook Time**	**Yield**
30 minutes	10 minutes	5

What you will need

- **Sesame seeds**, 1 tablespoon/0.3oz./9g
- **Spelt flour**, 3 cups/12.7oz./360g
- **Thyme**, 1 teaspoon/0.03oz./0.9g
- **Tomatoes (chopped)**, ½ cup/3oz./90g
- **Oregano**, ½ teaspoon/0.02/0.5g
- **Grape seeds oil**, 1 tablespoon/0.5oz./13.6ml
- **Onion powder**, 1 teaspoon/0.08oz./7.8g
- **Okra**, 1 cup/3.5oz./100g
- **Onion (chopped)**, ½ cup/3.4oz./97.1g
- **Salt**, ½ teaspoon/0.21/6.1g
- **Walnuts (chopped)**, ½ cup/2oz./58g

Directions

1. Take a medium-sized bowl, add spelt flour, salt, thyme, oregano, and onion powder, and mix all. Add splashes of warm water gradually while kneading the dough. Now leave the dough to rest for 5 minutes.

2. Now use a rolling pin to flatten the dough. Press the edges with your fingers.

3. Brush the parchment paper with grape seed oil, place the pizza dough in the oven and bake it for 8 minutes at 400°F or 200 °C. When the crust becomes crisp, remove it from the oven.

4. Now top it with onion slices, cooked okra, tomatoes, and sesame seeds. Sprinkle chopped walnuts over it.

5. Cut it into 4 slices and serve!

Nutritional Content

Calories 374kcal | **Crabs** 57.1g | **Protein** 13.4g | **Fat** 13.1g | **Fiber** 10g

Black Olives and Tomatoes Wrap

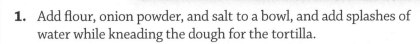

Prep Time
25 minutes

Cook Time
5 minutes

Yield
4

What you will need

- **Black olives**, 2 tablespoons/0.5oz./15g
- **White spelt flour**, 2 cups/8oz./240g
- **Onion powder**, 1 teaspoon/0.08oz./2.3g
- **Green bell pepper**, ½ cup/2.6oz./75g
- **Cherry tomatoes (chopped)**, ½ cup/3oz./90g
- **Savory**, ½ cup/3oz./92g
- **Onion (chopped)**, ½ cup/3.4oz./97.1g
- **Sea salt**, ½ teaspoon/0.11oz./3g

Directions

1. Add flour, onion powder, and salt to a bowl, and add splashes of water while kneading the dough for the tortilla.

2. Allow the dough to rest for 20 minutes. Meanwhile, add tomatoes, olives, bell peppers, salt, savory, and onion in a bowl.

3. Now use a rolling pin to flatten the tortilla into thin and round sheets. Bake the tortilla on the pan from both sides, until it cooks properly.

4. Apply tomato sauce to each tortilla and fill it with olives, tomatoes, and other vegetables

5. Wrap the tortilla after filling it and serve!

Nutritional Content

Calories 288kcal | **Crabs** 47.8g | **Protein** 9.8g | **Fat** 7.7g | **Fiber** 3.1g

Arugula and Sesame Wrap Seasoned with Achiote

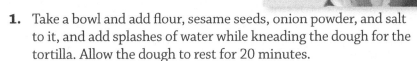

Prep Time
28 minutes

Cook Time
7 minutes

Yield
3

What you will need

- **Sesame seeds**, 2 tablespoons/0.6oz./180g
- **Wild arugula**, 1 cup/0.7oz./20g
- **Spelt flour**, 1 cup/4oz./120g
- **Onion powder**, ½ teaspoon/0.04oz./1.2g
- **Coconut flakes**, ¼ cup/0.7oz./20g
- **Purslane**, 2 tablespoons/0.19oz./5.4g
- **Cucumber (chopped)**, 1 cup/4.7oz./133g
- **Onion (chopped)**, ½ cup/3.4oz./97.1g
  - **Sea salt**, ½ teaspoon/0.11oz./3g
  - **Achiote seasoning**, 3 teaspoons/0.16oz./4.5g

Directions

1. Take a bowl and add flour, sesame seeds, onion powder, and salt to it, and add splashes of water while kneading the dough for the tortilla. Allow the dough to rest for 20 minutes.

2. Meanwhile, add arugula, coconut flakes, purslane, cucumber, and onion in a bowl.

3. Now use a rolling pin to flatten the tortilla into thin and round sheets. Bake the tortilla on the pan from both sides, until it cooks properly.

4. Apply achiote seasoning to each tortilla and fill it with arugula, coconut flakes, cucumber, and other vegetables.

5. Wrap the tortilla after filling it and serve!

Nutritional Content

Calories 238kcal | **Crabs** 36.6g | **Protein** 8.2g | **Fat** 8.4g | **Fiber** 7g

Wakame Seaweed Wraps

Prep Time
6 minutes

Cook Time
0 minutes

Yield
5

What you will need

- **Nori sheets**, 5 /0.5oz./14g
- **Green bell pepper**, ½ cup/2.6oz./75g
- **Wakame seaweed**, 4 tablespoons/0.7oz./20g
- **Cucumber (chopped)**, 1 cup/4.7oz./133g
- **Onion slices**, 1 cup/6.89oz./194g
- **Cayenne pepper**, 2 teaspoons/0.12oz./3.5g
- **Dill**, ½ cup/0.16oz./4.4g

Directions

1. Add onion, bell pepper, wakame seaweeds, chopped cucumber, and dill in a bowl.

2. Add cayenne pepper to a bowl. Mix all items well.

3. Take nori sheets, and fill each sheet with wakame mixture and vegetables equally.

4. Wrap all the sheets, stuffed with wakame mixture.

5. Serve and enjoy!

Nutritional Content

Calories 36kcal | **Crabs** 6.9g | **Protein** 2.1g | **Fat** 0.3g | **Fiber** 2.2g

Turnip and Zucchini Wrap

Prep Time
18 minutes

Cook Time
5 minutes

Yield
4

What you will need

- **Turnip greens**, 1 cup/5oz./144g
- **Zucchini**, 1 cup/7.4oz./210g
- **Spelt flour**, 2 cups/8.4oz./240g
- **Salt**, 1 teaspoon/0.04oz./1g
- **Hemp seeds**, 1 teaspoon/0.12oz./3.3g
- **Grape seeds oil**, 1 tablespoon/0.5fl. oz./13.6ml
- **Basil**, 1 teaspoon/0.03oz./0.9g
- **Onion (chopped)**, 1 cup/6.85oz./194g
- **Watercress**, ¼ cup/0.3oz./8.5g

Directions

1. Mix salt and flour in a bowl. Add warm water to knead the dough for wrapping the zucchini.

2. Allow the dough to rest for 8 minutes.

3. Add zucchini, watercress, turnip greens, hemp seeds, and onion in a bowl and mix all ingredients.

4. Now cut the dough into 4 pieces and bake them.

5. Fill each bread with a zucchini and watercress mixture. Sprinkle basil and spray grapeseed oil over it.

6. Wrap the bread stuffed with zucchini and turnip greens and serve with tomato sauce.

Nutritional Content

Calories 272kcal | **Crabs** 49.9g | **Protein** 10.5g | **Fat** 5.5g | **Fiber** 9.2g

Quinoa Bread Sandwich with Coconut Cheese and Arugula

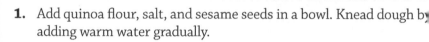

Prep Time
23 minutes

Cook Time
40 minutes

Yield
4

What you will need

- **Quinoa flour**, 1 cup/4oz./113.4g
- **Salt**, 1 teaspoon/0.21oz./6.1g
- **Sesame seeds**, 2 tablespoons/0.6oz./18g
- **Coconut cheese slices**, 1 cup/6.35oz./180g
- **Arugula**, 1 cup/0.7oz./20g
- **Cucumber slices**, 1 cup/4.2oz./119g
- **Tomato slices**, ½ cup/6.35oz./180g
- **Sesame oil**, 1 tablespoon/0.5fl. oz./13.6ml

Directions

1. Add quinoa flour, salt, and sesame seeds in a bowl. Knead dough by adding warm water gradually.

2. Knead until it becomes smooth. Set it aside for 10 minutes.

3. Now place the dough on a baking sheet coated with sesame oil. Bake it for 40 minutes at 350 °F or 176.6 °C, until the bread becomes a sponge.

4. Now remove from oven and cut the loaf into slices. Put arugula, cucumber and tomato slices, and coconut cheese slices in one slice of quinoa bread. Cover it with another slice and serve!

Nutritional Content

Calories 337.6kcal | **Crabs** 21.8g | **Protein** 16g | **Fat** 22.5g | **Fiber** 3.3g

Coconut Butter Sandwich with Tahini Sesame Butter

Prep Time
20 minutes

Cook Time
55 minutes

Yield
5

What you will need

- **Spelt flour**, 2 cups/8oz./240g
- **Agave syrup**, 1 tablespoon,0.74fl.oz./21ml
- **Salt**, 1 teaspoon/0.21oz./6.1g
- **Tahini sesame butter**, ¼ cup/1oz./30g
- **Coconut butter**, 3 tablespoons/4oz./113.4g
- **Cucumber slices**, 1 cup/4.2oz./119g
- **Onion (slices)**, ½ cup/3.42oz./97g
- **Tomato slices**, ½ cup/3oz./90g
- **Watercress**, 1 cup/5oz./142g

Directions

1. Add spelt flour, salt, and agave syrup in a bowl. Knead dough by adding warm water gradually. Knead until it becomes smooth. Set it aside for 10 minutes.

2. Now place the dough on a baking sheet coated with grapes seed oil.

3. Bake it for 55 minutes at 350 °F or 176.6 °C, until the bread becomes a sponge.

4. Now remove from oven and cut the loaf into slices. Apply coconut butter on each slice, and top it with cucumber, onion, and tomato slices. Add watercress and cover it with another slice.

5. Serve with tahini sesame butter and enjoy!

Nutritional Content

Calories 384.7kcal | **Crabs** 50.9g | **Protein** 10g | **Fat** 17.8g | **Fiber** 10g

Trumpet Mushroom Sandwich

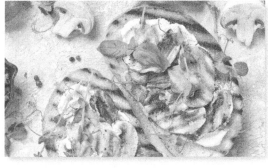

Prep Time
15 minutes

Cook Time
50 minutes

Yield
4

What you will need

- **Trumpet mushrooms**, 1 cup/7oz./200g
- **Quinoa flour**, 1 cup/4oz./113.4g
- **Salt**, 1 teaspoon/0.21oz./6.1g
- **Sesame seeds**, 2 tablespoons/0.6oz./18g
- **Tomato slices**, ½ cup/3oz./90g
- **Sesame oil**, 1 tablespoon/0.5fl. oz./13.6ml
- **Lettuce**, 1 cup/1.2oz./35g

Nutritional Content

Calories 247.6kcal | **Crabs** 32.5g |
Protein 8.2g | **Fat** 9.9g | **Fiber** 5.9g

Directions

1. In a bowl add quinoa flour, salt, and sesame seeds. Knead dough by adding warm water gradually. Knead until it becomes smooth. Set it aside for 10 minutes.

2. Meanwhile, take a saucepan and heat trumpet mushrooms in sesame oil. Stir continuously, until mushrooms become brown and crispy. Now set it aside.

3. Now place the dough on a baking sheet coated with sesame oil.

4. Bake it for 40 minutes at 350 °F or 176.6 °C, until the bread becomes a sponge. Now remove from oven and cut the loaf into slices.

5. Put crispy mushrooms, fresh lettuce, and tomato slices in one slice of quinoa bread. Cover it with another slice.

6. Serve with tomato sauce and enjoy!

Avocado and Green Olives Sandwich

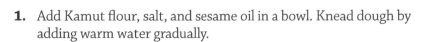

Prep Time
50 minutes

Cook Time
29 minutes

Yield
4

What you will need

- **Avocado**, 4 slices/6 tablespoons/2oz./60g
- **Green olives slices**, ½ cup/2.3oz./67.5g
- **Tomato slices**, ½ cup/3oz./90g
- **Kamut flour**, 1 cup/6.5oz./186g
- **Salt**, 0.5 teaspoon/0.11oz./3g
- **Sesame oil**, 1 tablespoon/0.5fl. oz./13.6ml
- **Cucumber slices**, 1 cup/4.2oz./119g

Directions

1. Add Kamut flour, salt, and sesame oil in a bowl. Knead dough by adding warm water gradually.

2. Knead until it becomes smooth. Set it aside for 20 minutes.

3. Now place the dough on a baking sheet coated with sesame oil. Bake it for 25 minutes at 350 °F or 176.6 °C, until the bread becomes a sponge.

4. Meanwhile, heat the olives and avocado for 4 minutes in the Pan., until they become soft. Now remove the Kamut bread loaf from the oven and cut it into slices

5. Fill the Kamut bread sandwich with avocado and olives slice. Add tomato and cucumber slices to it. Cover with another Kamut slice.

Nutritional Content

Calories 243.4kcal | **Crabs** 36.3g |
Protein 7.6g | **Fat** 9.4g | **Fiber** 7.2g

White Chickpea Sandwich with Tomatillo

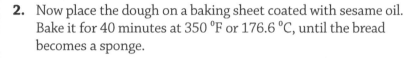

Prep Time
17 minutes

Cook Time
40 minutes

Yield
4

What you will need

- **White chickpeas (boiled)**, ½ cup/3oz./82g
- **Quinoa flour**, 1 cup/4oz./113.4g
- **Salt**, 1 teaspoon/0.21oz./6.1g
- **Sesame seeds**, 2 tablespoons/0.6oz./18g
- **Grape seed oil**, 1 tablespoon/0.5fl. oz./13.6ml
- **Cayenne pepper**, 2 teaspoons/0.12oz./3.5g
- **Tomatillo**, ½ cup/2.33oz./66g
- **Tomatoes (chopped)**, ½ cup/3oz./90g
- **Zucchini**, 1 cup/5oz./148.5g

Directions

1. Add quinoa flour, salt, and sesame seeds in a bowl. Knead dough by adding warm water gradually. Knead until it becomes smooth. Set aside for 10 minutes.

2. Now place the dough on a baking sheet coated with sesame oil. Bake it for 40 minutes at 350 °F or 176.6 °C, until the bread becomes a sponge.

3. Now remove from oven and cut the loaf into slices. Put white chickpeas, tomatillo, tomato, and zucchini slices in one slice of quinoa bread.

4. Sprinkle cayenne pepper on each slice. Cover all slices and serve!

Nutritional Content

Calories 212.3kcal | **Crabs** 28.4g | **Protein** 7.5g | **Fat** 8.4g | **Fiber** 5.3g

Mushroom Stuffed Wraps with Tahini Butter

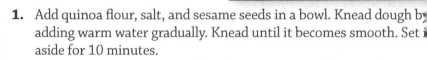

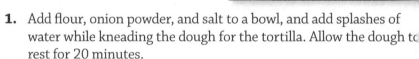

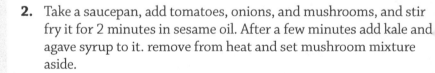

Prep Time
30 minutes

Cook Time
9 minutes

Yield
5

What you will need

- **Mushrooms**, 5 tablespoons/1.72oz./48.7g
- **White spelt flour**, 2.5 cups/10.5oz./300g
- **Onion powder**, 1 teaspoon/0.08oz./2.3g
- **Cherry tomatoes** (chopped), ½ cup/3oz./90g
- **Onion (chopped)**, ½ cup/3.4oz./97.1g
- **Sea salt**, ½ teaspoon/0.11oz./3g
- **Tahini butter**, 2 tablespoons/1 oz./32g
- **Kale**, 1 cup/0.74oz./21g
  - **Agave syrup**, ¼ cup/3oz./84g
  - **Sesame oil**, 1 tablespoon/0.5oz./13.6g

Directions

1. Add flour, onion powder, and salt to a bowl, and add splashes of water while kneading the dough for the tortilla. Allow the dough to rest for 20 minutes.

2. Take a saucepan, add tomatoes, onions, and mushrooms, and stir fry it for 2 minutes in sesame oil. After a few minutes add kale and agave syrup to it. remove from heat and set mushroom mixture aside.

3. Now use a rolling pin to flatten the tortilla into thin and round sheets. Bake the tortilla on the pan from both sides, until it cooks properly. Use a spatula to apply tahini butter to each tortilla. Fill each tahini butter tortilla with a mushroom mixture.

4. Wrap the tortilla after filling it and apply the remaining tahini butter on the upper surface. Serve and enjoy!

Nutritional Content

Calories 331.8kcal | **Crabs** 60.1g | **Protein** 10.7g | **Fat** 7.6g | **Fiber** 8g

Chapter-4
Beans, Grains and Pasta

Tik Tok famous pasta with Dr. Sebi's ingredients

 Prep Time 10 minutes

 Cook Time 30 minutes

 Yield 5

What you will need

- **Chickpea flour pasta**, 500g / 1lb.
- **1 onion chopped**, 150g
- **Sesame oil**, 3tablespoons, 45g
- **Cherry tomatoes**, 900g, 2 lb.
- **Date sugar**, 1 ½ teaspoon, 7.5g
- **Kale**, 2 cup, 135g
- **Alkaline vegan cheese**, 1 cup, 113g

Nutritional Content

Calories 314kcal | **Crabs** 35g | **Protein** 10g | **Fat** 15g | **Fiber** 13g

Directions

1. Preheat the oven to 350 degrees.

2. In a bowl add salt, and sesame oil to the onions. In another bowl add date sugar and tomatoes. Add the contents of this bowl and onions to a baking tray.

3. Pop this into the oven. Roast all these contents for 35 minutes until the onion is brown. Boil 500g of penne pasta in salted water halfway through. Save 1/3 of a cup of the pasta water.

4. Now combine the roasted onion, tomato, penne pasta, and pasta water in a pan and let it simmer for 2-3 minutes. Check to make sure the pasta is "Al dente".

5. Top it off with vegan cheese. Serve!

Home Runner Spaghetti

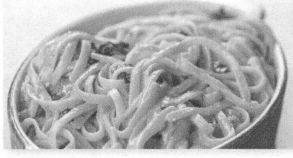

Prep Time
10 minutes

Cook Time
17 minutes

Yield
4

What you will need

- **Chopped cherry tomatoes**, 1 cup, 180g
- **Water**, ½ cup / 125ml
- **Sesame oil**, 3 tablespoon, 40ml
- **Basil leaves**, dried crushed, 1tablespoon, 3g
- **Capers**, 2 tablespoons, 17g
- **Fresh tomato juice**, 2 tablespoons, 30g
- **Dash of salt and cayenne pepper**
- **Vegan spaghetti**, 500g / 1lb.

Directions

1. In a pan add sesame oil and dried basil leaves, capers, tomato juice, and chopped tomatoes. Let this simmer. add water to prevent the tomatoes from drying out and to keep the sauce smooth.

2. In a separate pot add water for the spaghetti. Add salt to it. When the water is boiling add the spaghetti to it.

3. When the spaghetti has a bite to it, it is ready. Drain it and save ½ cup of spaghetti water.

4. Add the spaghetti water to the pan containing the tomato sauce. Let it cook for another 5 minutes finally add the pasta to this sauce

5. Serve!

Nutritional Content

Calories 224kcal | **Crabs** 22g | **Protein** 4.6g | **Fat** 14g | **Fiber** 4g

Tofu Chow Mein

Prep Time
15 minutes

Cook Time
10 minutes

Yield
6

What you will need

- **Tofu 1kg**, 2 lb.
- **3 onions**, 250g
- **Sesame tahini butter**, 2 tablespoons, 30g
- **Vegan light soy sauce**, 1 tablespoon, 15ml
- **Vegan dark soy sauce**, 1 tablespoon, 15ml
- **Oregano**, 2 tablespoons, 2g
- **Sesame oil**, 1 tablespoon, 15ml
- **Chickpea pasta**, 500g / 1lb.

Directions

1. Add chopped onion and oil to the wok. Then add oregano and tofu. Make sure the stove is not set on high. Let the onion cook until it is translucent.

2. In a separate pot boil the spaghetti for 3-4 minutes. Add the cooked spaghetti back to the wok.

3. Finally add vegan light soy sauce, vegan dark soy sauce, and sesame tahini butter to the wok to make the sauce.

4. Mix well. Serve!

Nutritional Content

Calories 360kcal | **Crabs** 29g | **Protein** 28g | **Fat** 16g | **Fiber** 5g

Cheesy Chickpea Pasta

 Prep Time
10 minutes

 Cook Time
20 minutes

 Yield
3

What you will need

- **Tofu 250g**, ½ lb.
- **Kale 2 cups**, 50g
- **Vegan cheese ¾ cup**, 80g
- **Chickpea pasta 1 ¼ cup**, 260g
- **Mushrooms 1 cup**, 70g
- **2 onions**, chopped, 150g
- **Basil**, fresh, chopped 1 tablespoon, 3g
- **Pinch of ground cayenne pepper**

Nutritional Content

Calories 256kcal | **Crabs** 27g |
Protein 15g | **Fat** 10g | **Fiber** 11g

Directions

1. Set a large saucepan of water on the stove to boil and preheat the grill to medium-high. Arrange the tofu and mushrooms on the grill rack and cook for 5 to 6 minutes.

2. Cook the pasta shapes in the boiling water for 9 minutes, then add the onions and kale and cook for a further 2 or 3 minutes.

3. Once the pasta, kale, and onions are cooked, drain them into the strainer, and spare 1 tablespoon of the cooking water in the pan.

4. Add vegan cheese into the hot saucepan with the reserved cooking water. Stir over medium heat until smooth. Then add the basil.

5. Return the pasta, tofu, mushrooms, and vegetables to the saucepan. Let the pasta simmer in the sauce for 3 minutes.

6. Mix gently to avoid the tofu breaking up too much. Sprinkle some cayenne pepper, then serve each portion with 1 teaspoon of vegan cheese on top.

Pesto pasta

 Prep Time
10 minutes

 Cook Time
20 minutes

 Yield
3

What you will need

- **Chickpea pasta**, 500g / 1lb.
- **Vegan cheese**, ½ cup, 65g
- **Walnut halves**, ½ cup, 50g
- **Olive oil**, 4 tablespoons, 54g
- **Basil leaves**, 2 cups, 48g
- **Salt to taste**
- **Cayenne pepper to taste**

Directions

1. In a blender add walnuts, basil leaves, and vegan cheese. Blend until this is smooth. Now add salt and pepper to it.

2. Finally, slowly add olive oil while the blender is running.

3. In a pot add water and bring it to a boil. Add salt to it. Then add vegan spaghetti to this water.

4. In a skillet add the sauce and boiled spaghetti. Cook the spaghetti in the sauce for 3 minutes and serve hot.

Nutritional Content

Calories 133kcal | **Crabs** 41g | **Protein** 16g |
Fat 13g | **Fiber** 6g

Tofu Marinara Pasta

Prep Time
14 minutes

Cook Time
30 minutes

Yield
4

What you will need

- **Tofu** ,500g, 1lb.
- **Salt**, ½ teaspoon, 2g
- **Basil**, ½ teaspoon, 1g
- **Fresh tomato puree**, ½ cup, 125g
- **Date sugar** ,1 teaspoon, 5g
- **Diced and stewed cherry tomatoes**, 1 cup, 150g
- **Chickpea pasta**, 1 ½ cup, 210g

Directions

1. In a skillet cook tofu over medium heat until browned.

2. Mix in stewed tomatoes, tomato puree, date sugar, and basil, and then simmer for around 19 minutes.

3. Boil salted water in a large pot. Add chickpea pasta and cook for 11 minutes or till it is well cooked then drain. Combine the pasta and tofu mixture and serve.

Nutritional Content

Calories 224kcal | **Crabs** 21g | **Protein** 20g | **Fat** 8g | **Fiber** 4.5g

Bell Pepper Pasta with Kale

Prep Time
6 minutes

Cook Time
9 minutes

Yield
4

What you will need

- **4 Bell peppers**, sliced 300g
- **Kale**, 2 cups, 45g
- **1 small onion**, 70g
- **Water**, 1.5 tablespoons, 40ml
- **Sesame oil**, 1.5 tablespoons, 20ml
- **Tamarind sauce**, 3 teaspoons, 22g
- **Himalayan pink salt**, (to taste)
- **Cayenne pepper**, ¼ teaspoon, 0.5g
- **Thyme**, ¼ teaspoon, 1g
  - **Peanuts**, 1 tablespoon, 10g
  - **Vegan pasta (gluten free)**, 500g / 1lb.

Directions

1. First, take a skillet and put sesame oil and heat it. Then add onion and fry them until changes to light pink.

2. Now add baby Bell pepper, kale, tamarind sauce, salt, and cayenne pepper to the skillet. Mix it nicely and cover it with a lid.

3. Boil pasta till it is "al dente". Let it cook for 2 minutes. Now remove the lid and add 500g boiled pasta. Cook for about 3 minutes until the kale turns soft.

4. Transfer to a bowl and sprinkle thyme and peanuts over it and enjoy.

Nutritional Content

Calories 267kcal | **Crabs** 36g | **Protein** 12g | **Fat** 9g | **Fiber** 6.8g

Kale Pasta

Prep Time
19 minutes

Cook Time
15 minutes

Yield
2

What you will need

- **Spelt pasta**, 1 cup/3oz./85g
- **Green bell pepper**, ½ cup/2.6oz./75g
- **Cherry tomatoes (chopped)**, ½ cup/3oz./90g
- **Onion (chopped)**, ½ cup/3.4oz./97.1g
- **Kale**, 1 cup/0.74oz./21g
- **Sea salt**, ½ teaspoon/0.11oz./3g

Nutritional Content

Calories 188.6kcal | **Carbs** 40g | **Protein** 7.1g | **Fat** 1.1g | **Fiber** 3.8g

Directions

1. Boil the spelt pasta for 15 minutes at medium flame, until it becomes soft.

2. Meanwhile cut the vegetables, onion, cherry tomatoes, and green bell pepper.

3. When the pasta is done, drain it for 5 minutes.

4. Add pasta to a chopped vegetable bowl. Add salt to it. Mix all the items well.

5. Now divide them into 2 bowls, and top them with cherry tomatoes and kale. Serve and enjoy!

Coconut Cheese Pasta

Prep Time
21 minutes

Cook Time
18 minutes

Yield
4

What you will need

- **Spelt pasta**, 2 cups/6oz./170g
- **Tomato sauce**, 2 tablespoons/1oz./30g
- **Cherry tomatoes (chopped)**, ½ cup/3oz./90g
- **Coconut milk**, ½ cup/4fl. Oz./120ml
- **Onion (chopped)**, ½ cup/3.4oz./97.1g
- **Coconut cheese**, ¼ cup/1oz./30g
- **Sea salt**, ½ teaspoon/0.11oz./3g
- **Thyme**, 1 teaspoon/0.03oz./0.9g

Directions

1. Take the saucepan and boil the spelt pasta for 15 minutes at medium flame, until it becomes soft.

2. Meanwhile, add thyme and salt to the coconut milk. In another bowl add onions and tomatoes to the tomato sauce.

3. Now mix the tomato sauce with coconut milk. Heat it for 3 minutes, until the tomatoes become soft.

4. When the pasta is done, drain it for 5 minutes. Add pasta to a mixed sauce. Sprinkle coconut cheese cubes over warm the pasta. Mix all items gently.

5. Pour them into 4 bowls and serve warm.

Nutritional Content

Calories 199kcal | **Carbs** 35.3g | **Protein** 7.9g | **Fat** 3.9g | **Fiber** 2.4g

Garbanzo Beans with Papaya

Prep Time
19 minutes

Cook Time
40 minutes

Yield
3

What you will need

- **Garbanzo beans**, 1 cup/5.78oz./164g
- **Papaya**, 1 cup/9oz./260g
- **Lettuce chopped**, 1 cup/1oz./36g
- **Onion powder**, 1 teaspoon/0.08oz./2.3g
- **Onion (chopped)**, ½ cup/3.4oz./97g
- **Tomatoes chopped**, ½ cup/3oz./90g
- **Oregano**, 1 teaspoon/0.04oz./1g
- **Achiote seasoning**, 2 teaspoons/0.11oz./3g
- **Olive oil**, 1 tablespoon/0.5fl.oz./13.5ml

Directions

1. Soak the bean for 6 hours. After soaking add them to water in a pan and bring it to a boil. Now reduce the flame and boil them at low flame for 35 minutes.

2. Meanwhile, take a bowl, and add lettuce, papaya, onion powder, oregano, chopped onion, and tomatoes to it.

3. When beans are done, remove them from heat, drain them and allow them to cool at room temperature. Now add beans to the papaya bowl, and mix all the items properly.

4. Season the bowl with achiote and olive oil dressing. Serve and enjoy!

Nutritional Content

Calories 192.8kcal | **Carbs** 30.4g | **Protein** 6.1g | **Fat** 6.3g | **Fiber** 6.9g

Mushroom Zucchini Pasta

Prep Time
6 minutes

Cook Time
10 minutes

Yield
4

What you will need

- **Spelt pasta**, 1 lb./454g
- **2 zucchinis**, sliced, quartered,
- **Thyme**, 2 sprigs
- **Cremini mushrooms**, sliced, 1 lb./454g
- **Cayenne pepper**, 2 teaspoons /10g
- **Sea salt**, two pinches or to taste
- **Coconut milk**, ¼ cup /59ml

Directions

1. In a large stockpot, mix the pasta, zucchini, mushrooms and water about 4 ½ cups, sprinkle cayenne and sea salt according to your taste.

2. Let it boil, once it starts boiling reduce the heat and let it cook for 10 minutes or more, till liquid Is reduced and pasta is cooked well.

3. Now mix in the coconut milk.

4. Serve warm.

Nutritional Content

Calories 465kcal | **Crabs** 84g | **Protein** 21g | **Fat** 2.1g | **Fiber** 7.3g

Chickpea Spaghetti

Prep Time
6 minutes

Cook Time
15 minutes

Yield
6

What you will need

- **Kamut spelt spaghetti**, boiled, 3 cups /681g
- **Chickpeas**, cooked, 2 cups /454g
- **Cherry tomato sauce**,(homemade), 1½ cups /340g
- **Mushrooms**, diced, 1 cup /227g
- **Red onion**, diced, 1½ cups /340g
- **Cherry tomatoes**, chopped, 1½ cups /340g
- **Oregano**, dried, ½ tablespoon /7g
- **Sea salt**, to taste
- **Grapeseed oil**, 1 tablespoon /15ml

Directions

1. In a large stockpot, mix the pasta, zucchini, mushrooms and water about 4 ½ cups, sprinkle. Sauté onions, chickpea in grapeseed oil, season with sea salt and cook for 5 minutes or till onions are translucent.

2. Now include water about 2 tablespoons or as needed to prevent vegetables from sticking.

3. Include mushrooms and sauté them for 2 minutes. Now add tomatoes and tomato sauce. Cook for 3 minutes more and adjust the seasoning according to your taste.

4. Put the sauce over pasta as much as you want and enjoy.

Nutritional Content

Calories 564kcal | **Crabs** 85.6g | **Protein** 22.7g | **Fat** 8.1g | **Fiber** 17g

Alkaline Chickpea Flour and Herb Bread

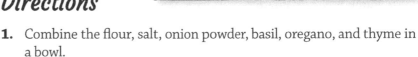

Prep Time
15 minutes

Cook Time
55 minutes

Yield
1loaf(16 slices)

What you will need

- **Chickpea flour**, 4 cups /908g
- **Basil**, 1 teaspoon /5g
- **Spring water**, 1 ½ cups /375ml
- **Oregano**, dried, 1 teaspoon /5g
- **Date syrup**, ½ cup/125ml
- **Onion powder**, 1 tablespoon /14g
- **Grapeseed oil**, 3 tablespoon /45ml
- **Sea salt**, 1 tablespoon /14g
- **Thyme**, 1 teaspoon /5g

Directions

1. Combine the flour, salt, onion powder, basil, oregano, and thyme in a bowl.

2. Now include date syrup and grapeseed oil in it and a cup of spring water mix it lightly.

3. It should be pourable and you can add more water if needed and if batter is too thick.

4. Grease the 9 x 5" pan with oil and pour batter in it.

5. Let it bake at 350 °F (180 °C) for 55 minutes or more. Cool it before serving.

Nutritional Content

Calories 138.5kcal | **Crabs** 17.3g | **Protein** 5.15g | **Fat** 4.09g | **Fiber** 2.48g

Kale and Chickpeas

Prep Time 16 minutes   **Cook Time** 40 minutes   **Yield** 2

What you will need

- **Kale**, 2 cups/1.5oz./42g
- **Chickpeas**, ½ cup/2.9oz./82g
- **Onion powder**, 1 teaspoon/0.08/2.3g
- **Thyme**, 1 teaspoon/0.03oz./0.9g
- **Cayenne pepper**, 2 teaspoons/0.12oz./3.5g
- **Sea salt**, ½ teaspoon/0.11oz./3g
- **Walnuts**, 1 tablespoon/0.26oz./7.3g
- **Avocado oil**, 1 tablespoon/0.5fl.oz./13.6ml
- **Agave syrup**, 2 tablespoons0.5fl.oz./42ml

Directions

1. Soak the chickpeas for 6 hours. After soaking, put them in a pan filled with water. Bring them to a boil.
2. Now reduce the heat and boil them at low flame for 40 minutes.
3. Meanwhile, add kale, onion powder, thyme, cayenne pepper, salt, and walnuts in a bowl.
4. When chickpeas become soft, mix them with the kale mixture. Toss them with agave syrup.
5. Gently mix chickpeas and kale.
6. Serve with a dressing of avocado oil.

Nutritional Content

Calories 117.3kcal | **Crabs** 15.5g | **Protein** 2.6g | **Fat** 5.5g | **Fiber** 2.5g

Mushrooms Pasta

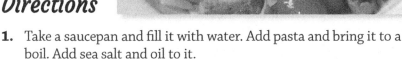

Prep Time 14 minutes   **Cook Time** 28 minutes   **Yield** 2

What you will need

- **Kamut pasta**, 1 cup/8oz./228g
- **Mushrooms**, 1 cup/3.39oz./96g
- **Cherry tomatoes**, 1 cup/4.8oz./136g
- **Onions (chopped)**, ¼ cup/1.71oz./48.5g
- **Onion powder**, 1 teaspoon/0.08oz./2.3g
- **Thyme**, 1 teaspoon/0.03oz./0.9g
- **Basil leaves (chopped)**, 1 tablespoon/0.09oz./2.7g
- **Sea salt**, 1 teaspoon/0.21oz./6g
- **Grape seed oil**, 2 tablespoons/1fl.oz./27.3ml

Directions

1. Take a saucepan and fill it with water. Add pasta and bring it to a boil. Add sea salt and oil to it.
2. Boil the pasta for 15 minutes. Meanwhile, roast the mushrooms, until they turn brown. Set them aside.
3. Sautee onion and whole cherry tomatoes in a saucepan, add salt, onion powder, basil leaves, and thyme to it. Stir it for 2 minutes.
4. When the pasta is done, mix them with the cherry tomato mixture. Add roasted mushrooms to it. Mix all items gently.
5. Serve and enjoy!

Nutritional Content

Calories 289.2kcal | **Crabs** 43.9g | **Protein** 9.3g | **Fat** 8.5g | **Fiber** 7g

Hemp Seeds Quinoa

Prep Time
12 minutes

Cook Time
15 minutes

Yield
5

What you will need

- **Quinoa**, 2 cups/12oz./240g
- **Walnuts (chopped)**, ¼ cup/0.88oz./25g
- **Hemp seeds**, 1 tablespoon/0.35oz./10g
- **Walnut milk**, 1 cup/8fl. Oz./236.6ml
- **Coconut flakes**, ¼ cup/0.71oz./20g
- **Agave syrup**, 1 tablespoon/0. 74fl.oz/21g
- **Purslane**, ½ cup/0.76oz./21.5

Directions

1. Add quinoa and water to a pot, boil it and then heat for 15 minutes at medium flame.

2. When the quinoa is done, remove it from the heat and allow it to cool at room temperature.

3. Now add chopped walnuts, walnut milk, coconut flakes, agave syrup, and Purslane to it.

4. Mix all the ingredients properly. Sprinkle hemp seeds over it. Serve and enjoy!

Nutritional Content

Calories 360.3kcal | **Crabs** 49.8g | **Protein** 12g | **Fat** 13.2g | **Fiber** 5.9g

Chapter-5
Vegetable Recipes

Sea Vegetable Quinoa In Sesame Oil

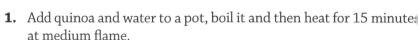

Prep Time
10 minutes

Cook Time
21 minutes

Yield
3

What you will need

- **Quinoa**, ½ cup/3oz./85g
- **Wakame**, 1 cup/2.82oz./80g
- **Cucumber slices**, 1 cup/4.2oz./119g
- **Tomato slices**, 1 cup/6.35oz./180g
- **Sesame oil**, 1 tablespoon/0.5fl. oz./13.6ml
- **Zucchini**, ½ cup/2.62oz./74.3g
- **Cayenne pepper**, 2 teaspoons/0.12oz./3.5g

Directions

1. Add quinoa and water to a pot, boil it and then heat for 15 minutes at medium flame.

2. Meanwhile, heat the sesame oil in a saucepan, and add wakame, zucchini, and cucumber slices. Stir them for 4 minutes. When the wakame is wilted, add tomato slices to it. Heat for another 2 minutes.

3. Now remove vegetables from heat. When the quinoa is done, shift it from the stove and mix it with vegetables.

4. After mixing well, sprinkle cayenne pepper over it. Serve and enjoy

Nutritional Content

Calories 179.1kcal | **Crabs** 25.2g | **Protein** 6g | **Fat** 6.9g | **Fiber** 3.7g

Roasted Mushrooms and Courgette

Prep Time
15 minutes

Cook Time
10 minutes

Yield
3

What you will need

- **Mushrooms**, 1 cup/2.5oz./70g
- **Courgette**, 1 cup/5oz./148g
- **Salt**, 1 teaspoon/0.21oz./6.1g
- **Cucumber (chopped)**, 1 cup/4.6oz./133g
- **Tomato (chopped)**, ½ cup/3oz./90g
- **Avocado oil**, 1 tablespoon/0.5fl. oz./13.6ml
- **Onion (chopped)**, 1 cup/6.85oz./194g
- **Yellow bell pepper (chopped)**, 1 cup/5oz./149g
- **Basil**, 1 teaspoon/0.02oz./0.7g
- **Dried oregano**, 1 teaspoon/0.04oz./1g

Directions

1. Heat avocado oil in a saucepan, and add mushroom, bell pepper, cucumber, and onion.

2. Stir them at the low-medium flame for 6 minutes, until mushrooms and vegetables are soft.

3. Now add tomatoes, courgettes, dried basil, oregano, and salt. Heat all for another 4 minutes.

4. Now remove from heat. Serve and enjoy!

Nutritional Content

Calories 104kcal | **Crabs** 13.9g | **Protein** 3.1g | **Fat** 5.1g | **Fiber** 3g

Avocado and Wakame

Prep Time
4 minutes

Cook Time
5 minutes

Yield
2

What you will need

- **Wakame**, 1 cup/2.82oz./80g
- **Avocado slices**, 3 /1.6oz./45g
- **Sesame oil**, 1 tablespoon/0.5fl. oz./13.6ml
- **Sesame seeds**, 2 teaspoons/0.21oz./6g
- **Onion powder**, 1 teaspoon/0.08/2.3g
- **Basil powder**, 0.5 teaspoon/0.01oz./0.3g
- **Green onion chopped**, 1 tablespoon/0.16oz./4.4g

Directions

1. Take a saucepan, and add sesame oil to it. When it starts to simmer, add wakame to it.

2. When wakame seaweed becomes wilted, add sesame seeds and onion powder, and cook for 3 minutes.

3. Add green onions and sweet basil powder. Heat all for 2 minutes and remove from heat.

4. Top it with avocado slices before serving. Serve and enjoy!

Nutritional Content

Calories 137.9kcal | **Crabs** 7.4g | **Protein** 2.4g | **Fat** 12.1g | **Fiber** 2.4g

Zucchini and Bell Pepper with Spices

Prep Time
16 minutes

Cook Time
0 minutes

Yield
3

What you will need

- **Red bell pepper**, 1 cup/5.26oz./149g
- **Yellow bell pepper**, 1 cup/5.26oz./149g
- **Green bell pepper**, 1 cup/5.26oz./149g
- **Zucchini**, 1 cup/5.24oz./148g
- **Cayenne pepper**, 2 teaspoon/0.12oz/3.5g
- **Cucumber slices**, 1 cup/4.2oz./119g
- **Avocado oil**, 1 tablespoon/0.5fl.oz./13.6ml
- **Dandelion greens**, 1 cup/1.94oz./55g
- **Achiote seasoning**, 1 teaspoon/0.05oz./1.5g

Directions

1. Add all bell peppers, chopped zucchini, and cucumbers in a large bowl.
2. Add chopped dandelion green to it. And mix all the vegetables well.
3. Season it with achiote seasoning. Sprinkle cayenne pepper over it.
4. Serve with avocado oil dressing and enjoy!

Nutritional Content

Calories 102kcal | **Crabs** 13.5g | **Protein** 2.9g | **Fat** 5.4g | **Fiber** 4.1g

Roasted kale

Prep Time
8 minutes

Cook Time
12 minutes

Yield
2

What you will need

- **Kale**, 2 cups/1.5oz./42g
- **Onion**, ½ cup/3.4oz./97g
- **Cucumber**, ½ cup/90g
- **Tomatoes**, (chopped) ½ cup/3oz./90g
- **Hempseeds oil**, 2 tablespoons/1fl. oz. /28ml
- **Sesame seeds**, 1 teaspoon/0.11oz./3g
- **Salt**, ½ teaspoon/0.11oz./3g
  - **Cayenne pepper**, 1 teaspoon/0.06oz./1.8g

Directions

1. Heat hempseed oil then add chopped onion, cucumber, and tomatoes into it. Add salt and cayenne pepper, and Sautee it for 5 minutes.
2. Now add kale to it and stir fry all vegetables for 7 minutes.
3. When kale becomes wilted, sprinkle sesame seeds.
4. Serve with tomato sauce and enjoy!

Nutritional Content

Calories 171.3kcal | **Crabs** 8.1g | **Protein** 1.9g | **Fat** 15.3g | **Fiber** 2.5g

Cucumber and Onion Salad with Hempseed Oil

Prep Time
13 minutes

Cook Time
0 minutes

Yield
2

What you will need

- **Salt**, 1 teaspoon/0.21oz./6.1g
- **Cucumber slices**, 1 cup/4.2oz./119g
- **Tomato slices**, 1 cup/6.35oz./180g
- **Onion sliced**, 1 cup/6.85oz./194g
- **Red bell pepper (sliced)**, ½ cup/75g
- **Yellow bell pepper (sliced)**, ½ cup/75g
- **Hempseeds oil**, 1 tablespoon/0.5fl. oz./13.6ml

Directions

1. In a bowl add sliced bell pepper, sliced onions and tomatoes, and chopped cucumber.

2. Mix all the items, add salt, and mix all vegetables again.

3. Do dressing of hempseeds oil.

4. Serve and enjoy!

Nutritional Content

Calories 142.8kcal | **Crabs** 18.3g | **Protein** 2.9g | **Fat** 7.6g | **Fiber** 4.5g

Boiled Mushrooms and Roasted Bell Peppers

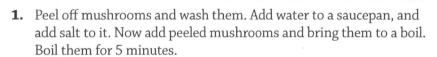

Prep Time
12 minutes

Cook Time
7 minutes

Yield
2

What you will need

- **Red bell pepper**, 1 cup/5.26oz./149g
- **Mushrooms**, 1 cup/2.5oz./70g
- **Salt**, 1 teaspoon/0.21oz./6.1g
- **Yellow bell pepper**, 1 cup/5.26oz./149g
- **Oregano powder**, 1 teaspoon/0.04oz./1g
- **Onion powder**, 1 teaspoon/0.08oz./2.3g
- **Green bell pepper**, 1 cup/5.26oz./149g
- **Avocado oil**, 2 tablespoons/1fl. oz./27.3ml
- **Agave syrup**, 1 teaspoon/0.25fl. oz. /7ml

Directions

1. Peel off mushrooms and wash them. Add water to a saucepan, and add salt to it. Now add peeled mushrooms and bring them to a boil. Boil them for 5 minutes.

2. Meanwhile, take another saucepan and heat avocado oil, add bell peppers, and stir fry it for a minute.

3. Add oregano, onion powder, and agave syrup to bell peppers. Heat them for another minute. Now remove from heat.

4. When mushrooms are boiled, drain them for 4 minutes. Add boiled mushrooms to roasted bell peppers. Mix all the items well.

5. Pour it into 2 small bowls. Serve and enjoy!

Nutritional Content

Calories 198.6kcal | **Crabs** 17.7g | **Protein** 3.4g | **Fat** 14.3g | **Fiber** 4.2g

Guacamole Salad

Prep Time
11 minutes

Cook Time
0 minutes

Yield
2

What you will need

- **Tomato slices**, 1 cup/6.35oz./180g
- **Avocados ripe**, 1 /4.8oz./136g
- **Onion sliced**, 0.5 cup/3oz./97g
- **Green bell pepper (chopped)**, 1 cup/5.26oz./149g
- **Avocado oil**, 1 tablespoon/0.5fl. oz./13.6ml
- **Fresh basil**, 1 tablespoon/0.05oz./1.5g
- **Sea salt**, ½ teaspoon/0.11oz./3g

Directions

1. Cut the avocado into 2 halves. Remove the seed.

2. Now fill the pit of avocado with chopped onions, tomatoes, and gree bell pepper. Add salt to it

3. Top it with fresh basil leaves.

4. Do dress with avocado oil.

5. Serve and enjoy!

Nutritional Content

Calories 224kcal | **Crabs** 17.4g | **Protein** 3.3g | **Fat** 17.7g | **Fiber** 7.7g

Squash and Walnuts Salad

Prep Time
9 minutes

Cook Time
25 minutes

Yield
4

What you will need

- **Walnuts (chopped)**, ½ cup/2oz./58.5g
- **Squash**, 2 cups, /10.5oz/297g
- **Onion (chopped)**, ½ cup/3.4oz./97g
- **Sesame oil**, 1 tablespoon/0.5fl. oz./13.6ml
- **Sesame seeds**, 1 tablespoon/0.32oz./9g
- **Habanero**, 1 teaspoon/0.18oz./5g
- **Dandelion greens**, 1 cup/2oz./55g
  - **Agave syrup**, ¼ cup/3fl.oz./85ml
  - **Cayenne pepper**, 1 tablespoon/0.19oz./5.3g

Directions

1. Brush the squash slices with sesame oil, place them in parchment pepper and place the baking tray in the oven.

2. Bake for 25 minutes at 350°F or 176.6°C, until the squash become brown and soft.

3. Meanwhile, chopped walnuts, onion, habanero, and Dandelion green in a bowl.

4. Remove the squash from the oven. Mix roasted squash with walnuts and vegetable bowl. Add cayenne pepper and agave syrup to it. Whisk all items properly.

5. Now serve with sprinkled sesame seeds and enjoy!

Nutritional Content

Calories 237kcal | **Crabs** 25.3g | **Protein** 4.3g | **Fat** 14.6g | **Fiber** 3.3g

Cherry Tomato and Okra Salad

Prep Time
16 minutes

Cook Time
9 minutes

Yield
3

What you will need

- **Salt**, 1 teaspoon/0.21oz./6.1g
- **Okra**, 1 cup/6.5oz./186g
- **Tomato slices**, 1 cup/6.35oz./180g
- **Onion sliced**, 1 cup/6.85oz./194g
- **Dill**, 1 cup/0.31/8.9g
- **Tarragon**, 3 tablespoons/0.19oz./5.4g
- **Red bell pepper (chopped)**,
  1 cup/5.26oz./149g
- **Achiote seasoning**, 1 teaspoon/0.05oz./1.5g
- **Basil**, 1 teaspoon/0.03oz./0.9g
- **Grape seed oil**, 2 tablespoons/1fl. Oz./27.3ml

Directions

1. Heat grape seed oil and add okra to it. Stir fry it for 9 minutes, until it becomes soft.

2. Meanwhile, take a large bowl, and add cherry tomatoes, bell peppers, dill, tarragon, basil, onion, and salt into it.

3. Remove okra from heat. Add okra to the cherry tomatoes bowl. Mix all items gently.

4. Season with achiote and pour it into 3 small bowls. Serve and enjoy!

Nutritional Content

Calories 158.3kcal | **Crabs** 17.5g | **Protein** 3.5g | **Fat** 9.7g | **Fiber** 4.9g

Vegetable and Mushrooms Stew

Prep Time
20 minutes

Cook Time
45 minutes

Yield
3

What you will need

- **Zucchini**, 1 cup/5.24oz./148.5g
- **Cucumber slices**, 1 cup/4.2oz./119g
- **Tomato slices**, 1 cup/6.35oz./180g
- **Onion sliced**, 1 cup/6.85oz./194g
- **Red bell pepper (chopped)**,
  1 cup/5.26oz./149g
- **Mushrooms**, 1 cup/3.4oz./96g
- **Oregano**, 2 teaspoons/0.13oz./3.6g
- **Basil**, 2 teaspoons/0.05oz./1.4g
- **Cayenne pepper**, 1 teaspoon/0.06/1.8g

Directions

1. Take a saucepan, fill it with spring water, and add zucchini, cucumber, onion, red bell pepper, and mushrooms. Bring it to a boil.

2. Add tomato into it and cook all at the low-medium flame for 35 minutes. Add basils, oregano, and cayenne pepper into it. Stir it continuously.

3. Cook the stew until its consistency becomes viscous and the mushrooms become dark in color.

4. Now remove from heat and pour it into 3 bowls. Serve and enjoy!

Nutritional Content

Calories 75.2kcal | **Crabs** 16.2g | **Protein** 3.8g |
Fat 0.8g | **Fiber** 4.6g

Dandelion Green and Butternut Squash Soup

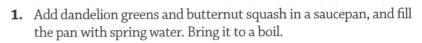

Prep Time
23 minutes

Cook Time
40 minutes

Yield
2

What you will need

- **Tomato slices**, 1 cup/6.35oz./180g
- **Onion sliced**, 1 cup/6.85oz./194g
- **Red bell pepper (chopped)**, 1 cup/5.26oz./149g
- **Butternut squash**, 1 cup/7oz./205g
- **Dandelion green**, 2 cups/3.88oz./110g
- **Onion powder**, 1 teaspoon/0.08oz./2.3g
- **Thyme**, 1 teaspoon/0.03oz./0.9g
- **Oregano**, 1 teaspoon/0.04oz./1g

Directions

1. Add dandelion greens and butternut squash in a saucepan, and fill the pan with spring water. Bring it to a boil.

2. Now add red bell peppers, onions, and tomatoes to boiling squash and dandelion greens. Reduce the heat to medium flame, cover it and leave it for 25 minutes.

3. Add onion powder, thyme, and oregano to the soup.

4. Stir it continuously for another 15 minutes. Now remove from heat when the soup becomes thick and pour into 2 bowls.

5. Serve with sea salt and enjoy!

Nutritional Content

Calories 146.6kcal | **Crabs** 34.4g | **Protein** 5.2g | **Fat** 1g | **Fiber** 9.8g

Chayote and Green Olives

Prep Time
13 minutes

Cook Time
0 minutes

Yield
2

What you will need

- **Chayote**, 1 cup/4.66oz./132g
- **Green olives (sliced)**, 0.5 cup/2.38oz./67.5g
- **Green onions**, ½ cup/1.25oz./35.5g
- **Yellow bell pepper**, 1 cup/5.26oz./149g
- **Fresh basils**, 1 tablespoon/0.09oz./2.7g
- **Olive oil**, 1 tablespoon/0.5fl.oz./13.6ml
- **Sea salt**, 1 teaspoon/0.21oz./6g

Directions

1. Add chayote, green olives, onions, and bell pepper in a bowl. Mix all vegetables.

2. Now add sea salt and fresh basil to it. Add achiote seasoning and toss all the vegetables.

3. Serve with olive oil dressing and enjoy!

Nutritional Content

Calories 146.4kcal | **Crabs** 10g | **Protein** 1.8g | **Fat** 12.3g | **Fiber** 3.2g

Amaranth Green and Garbanzo Beans

Prep Time
15 minutes

Cook Time
40minutes

Yield
2

What you will need

- **Amaranth greens**, 1 cups/1oz./28g
- **Garbanzo beans**, 1.5 cup/8.6oz./246g
- **Onion (chopped)**, ½ cup/3.42oz./97g
- **Green bell pepper**, 1 cup/5.26oz./149g
- **Cherry tomatoes**, 3 /1.8oz./51g
- **Sea salt**, ½ teaspoon/0.21oz./6g
- **Cayenne pepper**, 1 teaspoon/0.06oz./1.8g

Nutritional Content

Calories 246.6kcal | **Crabs** 43.8g |
Protein 12.7g | **Fat** 3.6g | **Fiber** 12.4g

Directions

1. Soak garbanzo beans for 6 hours. Bring them to a boil for 40 minutes. When beans become soft, remove them from heat and drain them.

2. Meanwhile, add amaranth greens, onion, bell pepper, and cherry tomatoes in a bowl.

3. Add beans to the vegetable bowl. Add sea salt and cayenne pepper over it. Toss the vegetables with beans properly.

4. After mixing gently, pour the salad into 2 bowls.

5. Serve and enjoy!

Kale and Dill Broth with Sautéed Vegetables

Prep Time
15 minutes

Cook Time
25 minutes

Yield
2

What you will need

- **Salt**, 1 teaspoon/0.21oz./6.1g
- **Tomato slices**, 1 cup/6.35oz./180g
- **Kale**, 2 cups/1.5oz./42g
- **Onion sliced**, 1 cup/6.85oz./194g
- **Dill**, 1 cup /0.31oz./8.9g
- **Green bell pepper (chopped)**, 1 cup/5.26oz./149g
- **Watercress**, 1 cup/1.2oz./34g
- **Turnip greens**, 1 cup/2oz./55g
- **Thyme**, 1 teaspoon/0.03oz./0.9g
- **Cloves**, 1 teaspoon/0.08oz./2.2g
- **Black olives**, ¼ cup/1.19oz./33.8g
- **Grape seed oil**, 2 tablespoons/1fl. oz. /27ml

Directions

1. Heat grape seed oil in the pan. Add onion, tomato, bell pepper, turnip greens, and watercress to it. Add salt and cloves to it. Sautee these vegetables for 10 minutes.

2. Meanwhile, add aqua fiber to the pan and add kale, dill, and black olives to it. Bring them to a boil.

3. Add sautéed vegetables to the boiling mixture and add thyme to it.

4. Heat all at high flame for 15 minutes. Now reduce the heat and stir it continuously.

5. Now remove from heat and serve with cayenne pepper.

Nutritional Content

Calories 238.6kcal | **Crabs** 22.5g | **Protein** 4.4g |
Fat 16.6g | **Fiber** 6.8g

Chapter-6
Fruit

Banana and Strawberry Smoothie

Prep Time
6 minutes

Cook Time
0 minutes

Yield
2

What you will need

- **Banana**, 2 /8oz./236g
- **Strawberries**, 1 cup/5oz./152g
- **Date sugar**, 2 teaspoons/0.28oz./8g
- **Fresh coconut milk**,
  2 cups/17fl.oz./480ml
- **Sesame seeds**, 2 teaspoons/0.21oz./6g

Directions

1. Add banana, coconut milk, fresh strawberries, and date sugar in a blender. Blend all the items.

2. Pour the smoothie into 2 bowls.

3. Top each bowl with banana and strawberry slices.

4. Sprinkle sesame seeds and serve!

Nutritional Content

Calories 199.4kcal | **Crabs** 37.7g | **Protein** 2.8g | **Fat** 6.6g | **Fiber** 5.5g

Blueberry Coconut Milkshake

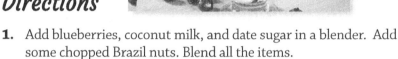

Prep Time
4 minutes

Cook Time
0 minutes

Yield
2

What you will need

- **Blueberries**, 1 cup/5.2oz./148g
- **Date sugar**, 2 teaspoons/0.28oz./8g
- **Fresh coconut milk**, 2 cups/17fl.oz./480ml
- **Brazil nuts**, 1 tablespoon/0.3oz./8.3g

Directions

1. Add blueberries, coconut milk, and date sugar in a blender. Add some chopped Brazil nuts. Blend all the items.

2. Pour the milkshake into 2 cups.

3. Top each bowl with remaining Brazil nuts.

4. Serve and enjoy!

Nutritional Content

Calories 122.5kcal | **Crabs** 15.4g | **Protein** 1.6g | **Fat** 7.5g | **Fiber** 2.7g

Herb and Apple Green Juice

Prep Time
8 minutes

Cook Time
0 minutes

Yield
3

What you will need

- **Spring water**, 2 cups/8fl.oz./237ml
- **Green apple**, 3 /15oz./420g
- **Savory leaves**, 0.5 cup/3.25oz./92g
- **Fresh basil**, 1 tablespoon/0.05oz./1.5g
- **Dandelion greens**, 1 cup/2oz./55g
- **Agave syrup**, 1 tablespoon/0.74fl.oz./21ml

Directions

1. Add all ingredients to a blender. Blend all items.

2. Sprinkle fresh basil leaves before serving.

3. Serve and enjoy!

Nutritional Content

Calories 184.8kcal | **Crabs** 28.8g | **Protein** 2g | **Fat** 8.3g | **Fiber** 4.8g

Apple and Hemp Seeds Milkshake

Prep Time
8 minutes

Cook Time
0 minutes

Yield
2

What you will need

- **Apples**, 1.5 cup/4.9oz./140g
- **Date sugar**, 2 teaspoons/0.28oz./8g
- **Hemp seeds milk**, 2 cups/17fl.oz./480ml
- **Hemp seeds**, 2 teaspoons/0.21oz./6g
- **Dates**, 2 /0.5oz./14g

Directions

1. Add peeled apples, date sugar, date without seed, and, hemp seeds milk in a blender. Blend all items for 2 minutes.

2. Pour the milkshake into 2 cups.

3. Sprinkle hemp seeds over it and serve!

Nutritional Content

Calories 181.6kcal | **Crabs** 18.9g | **Protein** 1.7g | **Fat** 8.5g | **Fiber** 2.5g

Papaya and Figs Smoothie In Walnut Milk

Prep Time
6 minutes

Cook Time
0 minutes

Yield
4

What you will need

- **Papaya (cubes)**, 2 cups/18.3oz./520g
- **Figs**, 1 tablespoon/0.27oz./7.6g
- **Walnut milk**, 4 cup/33.3fl. oz. /946ml
- **Walnuts (chopped)**, ¼ cup/4oz./117g
- **Agave syrup**, 2 tablespoons/1.5oz./42ml
- **Spring water**, 1 cup/8fl.oz./237ml

Directions

1. Add papaya, figs and agave syrup, and homemade walnut milk in a high-speed blender. Blend all items well.

2. Add spring water if the smoothie is thick.

3. Pour smoothie into 4 glasses. Top each glass with chopped walnuts

4. Serve and enjoy!

Nutritional Content

Calories 328.9kcal | **Crabs** 25.2g | **Protein** 6.5g | **Fat** 24.4g | **Fiber** 3.4g

Watermelon And Coconut Cheese With Basil

 Prep Time
7 minutes

 Cook Time
0 minutes

 Yield
2

What you will need

- **Watermelon (cubed)**, 2 cups/7oz./196g
- **Fresh basil leaves**, ½ cup/0.42oz./12g
- **Coconut cheese**, (cubed) 2 pieces/1oz./30g
- **Sea salt**, ½ teaspoon/0.11oz./3g
- **Avocado oil**, 2 tablespoons/1fl.oz./27.3ml

Directions

1. Cut the watermelon into cubes. Put them in a bowl, add coconut cheese over it

2. Now add salt and mix all items gently.

3. Top the watermelon bowl with fresh basil leaves.

4. Serve with avocado oil dressing and enjoy!

Nutritional Content

Calories 206.4kcal | **Crabs** 7.6g | **Protein** 4.3g | **Fat** 18.8g | **Fiber** 0.5g

Fruit Salad with Dandelion Greens

 Prep Time
5 minutes

 Cook Time
0 minutes

 Yield
2

What you will need

- **Strawberries (halved)**,
  1 cup/5.36oz./152g
- **Papaya (cubed) 1 cup/9oz./260g**
- **Watermelon cubed**, 1 cup/3oz./98.4g
- **Blueberries**, ½ cup/2.6oz./74g
- **Dandelion greens**, 1 cup/1.94oz./55g
- **Basil leaves**, 1 tablespoon/0.05oz./1.5g
- **Agave syrup**, 2 tablespoons/1.48oz./42g

Directions

1. Add all the fruits and basil leaves to a bowl. Mix all items gently.

2. Top it with dandelion greens and agave syrup.

3. Serve and enjoy!

Nutritional Content

Calories 193.7kcal | **Crabs** 47.6g | **Protein** 2.5g | **Fat** 1.1g | **Fiber** 5.8g

Creamy Mango and Grapes With Brazil Nuts

Prep Time
6 minutes

Cook Time
0 minutes

Yield
3

What you will need

- **Coconut cream**, 1 tablespoon/0.5oz./15.3g
- **Mangoes (cubed)**, 2 cups/16oz./458g
- **Grapes**, 2 cup/10.6oz./302g
- **Lettuce**, 1 cu1.2oz./35g
- **Date sugar**, 1 tablespoon/0.42oz./12g
- **Brazil nuts**, 1 tablespoon/0.29oz./8.3g

Directions

1. Add cubed mangoes, grapes, and lettuce in a bowl. Add date sugar to it.

2. Toss fruits with coconut cream. Mix all items gently.

3. Pour them into 3 small bowls.

4. Top each bowl with Brazil nuts and serve!

Nutritional Content

Calories 181.6kcal | **Crabs** 18.9g | **Protein** 1.7g | **Fat** 8.5g | **Fiber** 2.5g

Raspberry and Walnuts Quinoa

Prep Time
12 minutes

Cook Time
15 minutes

Yield
4

What you will need

- **Quinoa**, 1 cup/6oz./170g
- **Raspberry**, 2 cups/8.7oz./246g
- **Walnut (chopped)**, ½ cup/2oz./58.5g
- **Oregano**, 1 teaspoon/0.06oz./1.8g
- **Thyme**, 1 teaspoon/0.03oz/0.9g
- **Onion (chopped)**, ¼ cup/1.71oz./48.5g

Directions

1. Fill the pan with water, and add quinoa to it. Bring it to a boil. Now reduce the heat and cook quinoa for 15 minutes.

2. Meanwhile, take a medium-sized bowl, and add raspberry, some walnuts, chopped onion, oregano, and thyme to it. Mix all ingredients well.

3. When quinoa is cooked, remove it from the heat. Allow it to cool at room temperature for 15 minutes. Now add quinoa to the raspberry bowl. Mix all items gently.

4. Pour quinoa and raspberry into 4 bowls.

5. Top each bowl with chopped walnuts before serving. Serve and enjoy!

Nutritional Content

Calories 290.7kcal | **Crabs** 38.2g | **Protein** 9.2g | **Fat** 12.6g | **Fiber** 8.4g

Peach and Mango Juice

Prep Time
3 minutes

Cook Time
0 minutes

Yield
5

What you will need

- **Peaches**, (cubed) 4 /21oz./600g
- **Mangoes**, 4 cups/32oz./917g
- **Agave syrup**, ¼ cup/fl.3oz./84ml
- **Hemp seeds**, 1 tablespoon/0.35oz./10g
- **Spring water**, 1 cup/8fl.oz./237ml

Directions

1. Peel off the peaches and mangoes. Cut them into slices.

2. Now add peach and mango slices in a blender and, add agave syrup and spring water to it. Blend all items until they become smooth juice.

3. Pour them into 5 glasses

4. Sprinkle hemp seeds and serve!

Nutritional Content

Calories 219.5kcal | **Crabs** 52.3g | **Protein** 3.1g | **Fat** 1.8g | **Fiber** 5.3g

Cherries Pancakes in Avocado Oil

Prep Time
10 minutes

Cook Time
6 minutes

Yield
6

What you will need

- **Cherries**, 1 cup/5.4oz./154g
- **Walnut milk**, ½ cup/8fl. Oz. /118ml
- **Sesame tahini butter**,
  1 tablespoon/0.5oz./15g
- **Agave syrup**,
  3 tablespoons/2.2fl.oz./63ml
- **Kamut flour**, ½ cup/3.2oz./93g
- **Avocado oil**,
  2 tablespoons/1fl.oz./27.3ml

Directions

1. Mix walnut milk, agave syrup, tahini butter, and Kamut flour in a bowl. Mix all items properly until they are combined well.

2. Heat avocado oil in a pan, now put in the flour mixture, and cook for a minute, flip over the pancake to be cooked from another side. Remove the pancake from the heat.

3. Blend some cherries with agave syrup. Make it jam consistently thick.

4. Now top the pancake with fresh cherries and some blended cherries. Serve and enjoy!

Nutritional Content

Calories 193.7kcal | **Crabs** 47.6g | **Protein** 2.5g | **Fat** 1.1g |
Fiber 5.8g

Watermelon and Coconut Water Juice

Prep Time
3 minutes

Cook Time
0 minutes

Yield
1

What you will need

- **Watermelon**, 1 cup/3.5oz./98.4g
- **Coconut soft jelly water**, 1 cup/8fl. Oz./245ml
- **Fresh basil**, 1 teaspoon/0.05oz./1.5g
- **Date sugar**, 1 teaspoon/0.14oz./4g

Directions

1. Add watermelon, coconut water, and date sugar in a blender. Blend all the items.

2. Pour the juice into a cup

3. Top the cup with fresh basil leaves.

4. Serve and enjoy!

Nutritional Content

Calories 86.4kcal | **Crabs** 19.9g | **Protein** 2.4g | **Fat** 0.6g | **Fiber** 3.4g

Strawberry Muffins

Prep Time
22 minutes

Cook Time
20 minutes

Yield
5

What you will need

- **Strawberries**, 1 cup/5oz./152g
- **Agave syrup**, 1 tablespoon/0.74oz./21g
- **Mashed banana**, 2 teaspoons/0.33oz./9.4g
- **Walnut milk**, 1.25 cup/10fl.oz./295g
- **Spring water**, 2 tablespoons/1 fl. Oz/29.6ml
- **Coconut cream**, ½ cup/2oz./61g
- **Spelt flour**, 2 cups/8oz./240g
- **Brazil nuts**, 2 tablespoons/0.6oz./16g
- **Date sugar**, ½ cup/4oz./113.4g
- **Salt**, ¼ teaspoon/0.05oz./1.5g

Directions

1. Cut the strawberry into small pieces. Dip them in agave syrup and set them aside. Now take a large bowl, and add spelt flour, date sugar, and salt to it.

2. In another bowl mix walnut milk with mashed banana. Mix walnut milk mixture with spelt flour mixture. Mix all items gently until they are combined well. Add spring water if needed.

3. Add dipped strawberry slices to the flour mixture. Combine all ingredients well. Brush the muffin pans with sesame oil, and pour the batter into them. Bake muffins for 20 minutes at 400 °F or 200 °C, until they become spongy.

4. Now remove them from the oven. Top each muffin with coconut cream and fresh strawberries. Sprinkle Brazil nuts and serve!

Nutritional Content

Calories 322.5kcal | **Crabs** 63.3g | **Protein** 9g | **Fat** 7.3g | **Fiber** 7.8g

Avocado and Dates Smoothie

Prep Time
6 minutes

Cook Time
0 minutes

Yield
2

What you will need

- **Avocado (mashed)**, 1 cup/8oz./230g
- **Date sugar**, 2 teaspoons/0.28oz./8g
- **Fresh coconut milk**, 2 cups/17fl.oz./480ml
- **Sesame seeds**, 2 teaspoons/0.21oz./6g
- **Dates**, 2 /0.5oz./14g

Directions

1. Add avocado, coconut milk, and date sugar in a blender. Blend all the items.

2. Pour the smoothie into 2 bowls.

3. Top each bowl with dates.

4. Sprinkle sesame seeds and serve!

Nutritional Content

Calories 282.2kcal | **Crabs** 20.1g | **Protein** 3.4g | **Fat** 23.7g | **Fiber** 9.3g

Black Currants and Pear Salad

Prep Time
6 minutes

Cook Time
0 minutes

Yield
3

What you will need

- **Pear**, 2 cups/22oz./628g
- **Date sugar**, 2 teaspoons/0.28oz./8g
- **Black currants**, ½ cup/1.98oz./56g
- **Coconut cream**, 2 tablespoons/1oz./30g
- **Sesame seeds**, 2 teaspoons/0.21oz./6g

Directions

1. Add all the ingredients to a bowl. Mix them gently.

2. Pour into 3 small bowls.

3. Sprinkle sesame seeds and serve!

Nutritional Content

Calories 169.8kcal | **Crabs** 40.2g | **Protein** 1.8g | **Fat** 2.2g | **Fiber** 8.4.g

Chapter-7
Sauces, Dips and Dressings

Chunky Guacamole Dip

Prep Time
4 minutes

Cook Time
0 minutes

Yield
3

What you will need

- **Avocado**, ripe, remove the pit, 1.5 cups/225 g
- **Cherry tomatoes**, chopped, ¼ cup/45g
- **Sesame oil**, 3 teaspoons /15ml
- **Lime juice**, 3.5 teaspoons/16.8g
- **Onion powder**, ¼ teaspoon /0.6g
- **Sweet basil**, ¼ teaspoon
- **Pure sea salt**, to taste
  - **Cayenne pepper**, grounded, to taste

Directions

1. To make this healthy dip, mash the ripe avocado in a small bowl.

2. Then put lemon juice, onion powder, sesame oil, sea salt, and cayenne pepper.

3. Now put chopped cherry tomatoes and sweet basil. Mix nicely.

4. Now transfer it to a ramekin bowl and enjoy!

5. Store the chunky guacamole dip in an airtight container in the refrigerator.

Nutritional Content

Calories 173.4kcal | **Carbs** 8.5g | **Protein** 1.8g | **Fat** 16.1g | **Fiber** 5.5g

Creamy Alkaline Ranch Dressing

Prep Time
4 minutes

Cook Time
0 minutes

Yield
4

What you will need

- **Spring water**, 2 tablespoons /30ml
- **Avocado oil**, 4 tablespoons /54.5ml
- **Lime juice**, fresh, 2 tablespoons/30g
- **Hemp seeds**, 5 teaspoons/16.7g
- **Onion**, chopped, 3 teaspoons/10g
- **Ginger powder**, ground, ¼ teaspoon/ 0.4g
- **Pure sea salt**, to taste
- **Thyme**, ¼ teaspoon /0.2g

Directions

1. To make this dressing, put the ingredients in a top-notch blender.

2. Now blend for a few seconds until the dressing reaches smooth consistency.

3. Store the dressing in an airtight container in the refrigerator.

Nutritional Content

Calories 146.9kcal | **Carbs** 1.3g | **Protein** 1.4g | **Fat** 15.7g | **Fiber** 0.3g

Sweet and Sour Orange Ginger Sauce

Prep Time
4 minutes

Cook Time
14 minutes

Yield
4

What you will need

- **Orange juice**, freshly squeezed, ¾ cup/186g
- **Ginger**, finely chopped, 1.5 teaspoons/10.1g
- **Lime juice**, fresh, 1 teaspoon/5g
- **Shallots**, chopped, 2 teaspoons/6.7g
- **Habanero**, ¼ teaspoon/0.7g
- **Pure sea salt**, to taste

Directions

1. To make this sauce, put the ingredients in a small saucepan. Mix nicely.

2. Allow it to boil and cook on low flame for 14 minutes. Keep stirring in between.

3. Now pour the sauce in a ramekin bowl and let it cool. Enjoy!

4. Store the dip in an airtight container in the refrigerator.

Nutritional Content

Calories 24.5kcal | **Carbs** 5.7g | **Protein** 0.4g | **Fat** 0.1g | **Fiber** 0.2g

Alkaline Garlic Dip Sauce

Prep Time 4 minutes   **Cook Time** 0 minutes   **Yield** 4

What you will need

- **Onion powder**, 2 teaspoons/0.16oz./4.6g
- **Dill powder**, 1 teaspoon/0.04oz./1g
- **Grape seed oil**, 2 tablespoons/1fl. oz./27.3ml
- **Ginger**, 1 teaspoon/0.06oz./1.7g
- **Sea salt**, 1 teaspoon/0.21oz./6g
- **Onion chopped**, ½ cup/3oz./97.1g

Directions

1. Add all onion powder, chopped onion, dill powder, salt, oil, and ginger to a blender and blend them for 2 minutes, until it becomes a creamy sauce.

2. Serve this alkaline garlic sauce with pasta and pizza.

3. Enjoy!

Nutritional Content

Calories 76kcal | **Crabs** 3.6g | **Protein** 0.5g | **Fat** 6.9g | **Fiber** 0.6g

Elderberry Syrup Dressing

Prep Time 5 minutes   **Cook Time** 25 minutes   **Yield** 3

What you will need

- **Elderberry**, ½ cup/2.56oz./72.5g
- **Spring water**, 2.5 cups/20fl.oz./592ml
- **Agave syrup**, ¼ cup/2.96fl.oz./84ml

Directions

1. Add elderberry and water in a saucepan and bring it to a boil.

2. Now reduce the heat and cover it. Boil elderberry at low medium flame for 20 minutes, until they are soft to be crushed with a spoon.

3. Stir elderberry and use a spatula to crush them.

4. Now strain the elderberry with the sieve.

5. Add agave syrup to elderberry liquid for taste. Serve as a dressing for different fruit salads.

Nutritional Content

Calories 104.4kcal | **Crabs** 25.8g | **Protein** 0.2g | **Fat** 0.2g | **Fiber** 1.7g

Homemade Hemp Seed Butter

 Prep Time
15 minutes

 Cook Time
0 minutes

 Yield
6

What you will need

- **Fresh apple slices**, 2 cups/8.8oz./250g
- **Hemp seeds hulled**, 1 cup/5.6oz./160g
- **Agave syrup**, ¼ cup/2.96fl. oz. /84ml

Nutritional Content

Calories 212.5kcal | **Crabs** 18.8g |
Protein 8.5g | **Fat** 13.1g | **Fiber** 2.1g

Directions

1. Add hulled hemp seeds in a high-speed blender. Blend it for 2 minutes, have a break of 3 minutes, and then blend again for another 5 minutes until it becomes smooth texture butter.

2. Now pour the butter into a bowl, add agave syrup and mix with help of a spoon.

3. Dip fresh apple slices in it. Serve this dipped apple in hemp seeds butter and enjoy!

4. It can serve as a dip for other fresh fruits

Creamy Avocado Dip with Mango

 Prep Time
10 minutes

 Cook Time
0 minutes

 Yield
5

What you will need

- **Walnut milk**, ½ cup/4fl. Oz. /118ml
- **Avocado (ripe)**, 2 /9.6oz./272g
- **Thyme**, ½ teaspoon/0.02oz./0.4g
- **Sage ground**, ½ teaspoon/0.01oz./0.3g
- **Cayenne pepper**, 1/8 teaspoon/0.01oz./0.2
- **Sea salt**, ¼ teaspoon/0oz./0.1g
- **Mangoes**, 1 cup/8oz./229g

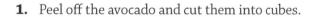

Directions

1. Peel off the avocado and cut them into cubes.

2. Now add avocado cubes, walnut milk, thyme, cayenne pepper, sea salt, and sage in a blender and blend all the items for 3 minutes. Give rest to the machine and blend again for another 3 minutes, until it becomes a creamy smooth mixture.

3. Now pour the creamy avocado dip into a bowl.

4. Serve with mangoes and enjoy!

Nutritional Content

Calories 220kcal | **Crabs** 20.3g | **Protein** 2.9g |
Fat 16.1g | **Fiber** 7.5g

Marinara Sauce

Prep Time
20 minutes

Cook Time
45 minutes

Yield
4

What you will need

- **Kamut pasta**, 2 cups/16oz./456g
- **Tomatoes**, 10 /21oz./615g
- **Onion powder**, 1 teaspoon/0.08oz./2.3g
- **Oregano**, 2 teaspoons/0.07oz./2g
- **Avocado oil**, 1fl.oz./27ml
- **Fresh basil**, 2 teaspoons/0.03oz./0.9g
- **Sea salt**, 1 teaspoon/0.42oz./12g
- **Red pepper**, ½ cup/2.6oz./74.5g
- **Onion**, ½ cup/3.4oz./97.1g
- **Habanero**, 1 teaspoon/0.18oz./5g

Directions

1. Boil Kamut pasta for 15 minutes, add oil and salt to it.

2. Meanwhile, take a bowl, cut tomatoes into it, and add basil, onion, red bell pepper, salt, and avocado oil. Toss them well. Place them on baking paper coated with oil. Roast this tomato mixture in preheated oven at 400°F or 204°C for 30 minutes.

3. Now remove from oven and allow it to cool at room temperature.

4. Add this roasted tomato mixture in a blender, and add oregano, habanero, and remaining basil to it. Blend all the items well, until they become smooth.

5. Pour the sauce into a bowl. Add pasta to the plate and top it with this roasted tomato sauce. Enjoy!

Nutritional Content

Calories 527kcal | **Crabs** 90.2g | **Protein** 17.9g | **Fat** 10.2g | **Fiber** 14.9

Tahini Sauce

Prep Time
6 minutes

Cook Time
4 minutes

Yield
4

What you will need

- **Kale**, 2 cups/1.5oz./42g
- **Avocado oil**, 2 tablespoons/1fl. Oz. /27.3ml
- **Sesame seeds**, 1 cup/5oz./144g

Directions

1. Put sesame seeds in a high-speed blender, add 2 teaspoons of avocado oil to it and blend it for a minute. Give some rest to a blender and then blend again for 2 minutes, until it acquires the consistency of a creamy paste.

2. Pour the tahini sauce into a bowl.

3. Now add avocado oil to a saucepan and heat it. Add kale and stir fry it for 3 minutes, until they are roasted.

4. Remove kale from heat and serve with tahini sauce.

Nutritional Content

Calories 270kcal | **Crabs** 8.9g | **Protein** 6.7g | **Fat** 24.9g | **Fiber** 4.7g

Habanero Sauce with Roasted Mushrooms

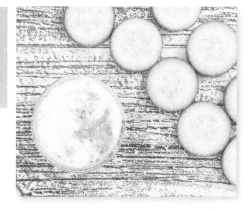

Prep Time
14 minutes

Cook Time
8 minutes

Yield
3

What you will need

- **Mushrooms**, 1 cup/3.4oz./96g
- **Grape seed oil**, 2 tablespoons/1fl. Oz. /27.3ml
- **Onion (chopped)**, ½ cup/3oz./97g
- **Green bell pepper**, ½ cup/2.6oz./74.5g
- **Thyme**, 1 teaspoon/0.03oz./0.9g
- **Sage**, 1 teaspoon/0.02oz./0.7g
- **Sea salt**, 1 teaspoon/0.21oz./6g
- **Habanero**, 3 /0.5oz./15g
- **Lime juice**, 2 tablespoons /1fl. Oz./30.3g

Directions

1. Roast the mushrooms in avocado oil and set them aside.

2. Now sauté the pepper and onion in grape seed oil, and add habanero and salt to it. Stir fry for 4 minutes.

3. Now remove it from heat and allow it to cool at room temperature.

4. Now add sauté vegetables in a blender, and add salt, thyme, sage, and lime juice to it. Blend all the items, until it becomes a smooth sauce.

5. Pour the habanero sauce into a bowl. Serve mushrooms with habanero sauce and enjoy.

Nutritional Content

Calories 114.3kcal | **Crabs** 6.4g | **Protein** 1.7g | **Fat** 9.3g | **Fiber** 1.5g

Cucumber Sage Dressing on Fruit Salad

Prep Time
13 minutes

Cook Time
0 minutes

Yield
4

What you will need

- **Cucumber**, 1 cup/4.2oz/119g
- **Sage**, 1 tablespoon/0.07oz./2g
- **Date sugar**, 2 teaspoons/0.42oz./12g
- **Grape seed oil**, 1 tablespoon/0.5fl. oz./13.6ml
- **Lime juice**, 1 tablespoon/0.5fl. oz. /15ml
- **Apple**, ½ cup/2oz./62g
- **Grapes**, 1 cup/5.3oz./151g
- **Mangoes**, 1 cup/8oz./229g
- **Banana**, 1 /4.8oz./136g

Directions

1. Blend, cucumber, sage, date sugar, oil, and lime juice in a blender, until it becomes smooth.

2. Cut, apples, bananas, grapes, and mangoes in a bowl.

3. Serve fruit salad with cucumber age dressing.

Nutritional Content

Calories 142kcal | **Crabs** 29.1g | **Protein** 1.4g | **Fat** 3.9g | **Fiber** 3.2g

Garbanzo Beans with Papaya Dressing

 Prep Time
15 minutes

 Cook Time
45 minutes

 Yield
3

What you will need

- **Garbanzo beans**, 1 cup/5.8oz./164g
- **Thyme**, 2 teaspoons/0.06oz./1.8g
- **Papaya**, 1 cup/9oz./259g
- **Lime**, 1 tablespoon/0.5fl. oz. /15ml
- **Sea salt**, 1 teaspoon/0.21oz./6.1g

Directions

1. Peel off the papaya, and cut them into cubes. Put papaya, lime, salt, thyme, and oregano in a blender. Blend all items until it becomes smooth.

2. Now pour papaya dressing into a bowl.

3. Soak garbanzo beans for 6 hours. After soaking, add beans to a pan filled with water. Bring them to a boil. Boil them for 30 minutes.

4. When beans become soft, remove them from heat.

5. Serve beans with papaya dressing and enjoy!

Nutritional Content

Calories 129.8kcal | **Crabs** 25.2g | **Protein** 5.3g | **Fat** 1.7g | **Fiber** 5.9g

Basil pesto

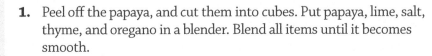

 Prep Time
6 minutes

 Cook Time
16 minutes

 Yield
3

What you will need

- **Spelt pasta**, 1 cup/3oz./85g
- **Fresh basil**, ¼ cup/0.37oz./10.6g
- **Walnuts (chopped)**, 1 tablespoon/0.26oz./7.3g
- **Sea salt**, 1 teaspoon/0.21oz./6g
- **Lime juice**, 1 tablespoon/0.5fl.oz./15ml

Directions

1. Boil pasta for 15 minutes, add salt and oil to it.

2. Meanwhile add fresh basil, walnuts, lime juice, and sea salt to a blender. Blend them, until they become smooth.

3. Drain the pasta and pour them onto the plate.

4. Serve pasta top with basil pesto

Nutritional Content

Calories 118kcal | **Crabs** 21.9g | **Protein** 4.2g | **Fat** 2.1g | **Fiber** 1.2g

Strawberry and Dandelion Greens with Agave Syrup

Prep Time
15 minutes

Cook Time
0 minutes

Yield
3

What you will need

- **Strawberries**, 1 cup/5.36oz./152g
- **Basil leaves**, ½ cup/0.42oz./12g
- **Dandelion greens**, ½ cup/1oz./28g
- **Sesame seeds**, 1 teaspoon/0.11oz./3g
- **Coconut cheese**, 4 cubes/2oz./58g
- **Walnut halves**, ¼ cup/½ cup/0.88oz./25g
- **Agave nectar**, ¼ cup/2.96oz./84g
- **Hot water**, ¼ cup. /2fl.oz./59ml

Directions

1. For agave syrup, mix agave nectar with hot water, stir it well, and set it aside.

2. Take a bowl and add strawberries, dandelion green, fresh basils, sesame seeds, coconut cheese, and walnuts.

3. Toss the strawberry bowl with agave syrup and serve!

Nutritional Content

Calories 161.5kcal | **Crabs** 27.6g | **Protein** 2.2g | **Fat** 6.2g | **Fiber** 2.1g

Creamy Hemp and Walnut Dressing on The Salad

Prep Time
12 minutes

Cook Time
0 minutes

Yield
4

What you will need

- **Walnuts**, ¼ cup/0.88oz./25g
- **Hemp seeds hulled**, 1 cup/5.6oz./160g
- **Tomatoes (chopped)**, ½ cup/3oz./90g
- **Onion (sliced)**, ½ cup/3.4oz./97g
- **Yellow bell pepper**, ½ cup/2.6oz./74.5g
- **Dandelion greens**, ½ cup/1oz./28g
- **Lime**, 1 / 2.4oz. /67g
- **Avocado oil**, 1 tablespoon/0.5fl. oz. /13ml

Directions

1. Add hulled hemp seeds and oil in a high-speed blender. Blend it for 2 minutes, have a break of 3 minutes, and then blend again for another 5 minutes until it becomes smooth texture cream.

2. Now pour the cream into a bowl and set them aside.

3. Add tomato, onion, hemp seeds, yellow bell pepper, dandelion greens, and lime slices on a plate.

4. Top the plate with creamy hemp seeds and walnut dressing. Serve and enjoy!

Nutritional Content

Calories 319kcal | **Crabs** 11g | **Protein** 14.5g | **Fat** 27.2g | **Fiber** 3.5g

Quick Walnut Butter

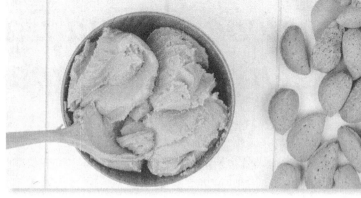

Prep Time	**Cook Time**	**Yield**
8 minutes	10 minutes	3

What you will need

- **Strawberries**, 1 cup/5.3oz./152g
- **Walnuts**, 0.5 cup/1.76oz./50g
- **Agave syrup**, ¼ cup/0.5fl. oz. /14ml
- **Sea salt**, ¼ teaspoon/0.05oz./1.5g

Directions

1. Add walnuts to a baking sheet and place them in preheated oven at 350°F or 176.6°C for 10 minutes. Roast the walnuts. Remove them from the oven. Allow them to cool.

2. Now add roasted walnuts, salt, and agave syrup in a food processor. Blend all items, until a smooth butter texture appears.

3. Pour butter into a small bowl.

4. Serve strawberries dip in walnut butter and enjoy!

Nutritional Content

Calories 139.7kcal | **Crabs** 9.7g | **Protein** 2.9g | **Fat** 11g | **Fiber** 2.1g

Quinoa with Strawberry Syrup Dressing

Prep Time	**Cook Time**	**Yield**
18 minutes	25 minutes	3

What you will need

- **Strawberries**, 1 cup/5.3oz./152g
- **Quinoa**, 1 cup/6oz./170g
- **Agave syrup**, ¼ cup/0.5fl. oz. /14ml
- **Lime juice**, 1 tablespoon/0.5fl.oz./15ml
- **Coconut oil**, 1 tablespoon/0.5fl.oz. /14ml

Directions

1. Add quinoa to a saucepan filled with water. Add salt to it and bring it to a boil.

2. Reduce heat and boil it at low flame for 25 minutes.

3. Meanwhile, add strawberries, agave syrup, lime juice, and coconut oil in a blender. Blend all the items, until it becomes a smooth mixture.

4. When quinoa is done, dish it out. Serve quinoa with strawberry syrup dressing.

5. Sprinkle some fresh strawberries over it and enjoy!

Nutritional Content

Calories 118kcal | **Crabs** 21.9g | **Protein** 4.2g | **Fat** 2.1g | **Fiber** 1.2g

Pepper Hummus Sauce with Quinoa

Prep Time
17 minutes

Cook Time
28 minutes

Yield
5

What you will need

- **Quinoa**, 1 cup/6oz./170g
- **Red bell pepper**, ½ cup/2.6oz./74.5g
- **Agave syrup**, ¼ cup/2.96oz./84ml
- **Tahini**, 2 tablespoons/1oz./30g
- **Lime juice**, 1 tablespoon/0.5fl.oz./15ml
- **Coconut oil**, 1 tablespoon/0.5fl.oz. /14ml
- **Garbanzo beans**, ½ cup/5.8oz./164g

Directions

1. Add quinoa to a saucepan filled with water. Add salt to it and bring it to a boil. Reduce heat and boil it at low flame for 25 minutes.

2. Add red bell paper to a saucepan and roast it for 2 minutes, until the skin becomes soft and remove easily.

3. Now add tahini, coconut oil, agave syrup, lime juice, skin-removed red bell pepper, and garbanzo beans in a blender and blend all items until it becomes a creamy smooth sauce.

4. Dish out quinoa, when it is done. Pour the hummus sauce into a bowl.

5. Serve sauce with quinoa and enjoy!

Nutritional Content

Calories 295.6kcal | **Crabs** 46.1g | **Protein** 8.9g | **Fat** 9g | **Fiber** 5.8g

Peach Dipped in Cucumber and Avocado Dip

Prep Time
10 minutes

Cook Time
0 minutes

Yield
3

What you will need

- **Peach**, 3 /10.5oz./300g
- **Cucumber**, ½ cup/2.3oz./66g
- **Avocado**, ½ /2.4oz./68g
- **Avocado oil**, 2 tablespoons/0.5fl. oz./13.6ml
- **Date sugar**, 3 teaspoons/0.4oz./12g

Directions

1. Peel off cucumber and avocado, and cut them into cubes.

2. Add cubed cucumber, oil, avocado, and date sugar in a food processor. Blend all the items, until a smooth butter texture appears.

3. Pour the cucumber and avocado dip into a bowl.

4. Serve peach slices dipped in cucumber and avocado dip. Enjoy!

Nutritional Content

Calories 129.2kcal | **Crabs** 15.3g | **Protein** 1.5g | **Fat** 8.3g | **Fiber** 3.5g

Mushroom Hemp Sauce with Wild Rice

Prep Time
14 minutes

Cook Time
10 minutes

Yield
4

What you will need

- **Mushrooms**, 1 cup/3.39oz./96g
- **Hemp seeds**, ¼ cup/1.4oz./40g
- **Cayenne pepper**, 2 teaspoons/0.12oz./3.5g
- **Sage**, 1 teaspoon/0.02oz./0.7g
- **Thyme**, 1 teaspoon/0.03oz./0.9g
- **Oregano**, 1 teaspoon/0.04oz./1g
- **Wild rice**, 1 cup/5.6oz./160g
- **Coconut oil**, 1 tablespoon/0.5fl. oz. /13.6ml

Directions

1. Roast the mushrooms in grape seed oil for 4 minutes, until they become dark color and soft. Now remove them from heat and set them aside.

2. Now boil the wild rice in salty water, reduce the heat and cook them on low flame for 5 minutes.

3. Meanwhile, add hempseeds and oil to the blender and blend it for 2 minutes. Now add roasted mushrooms, cayenne pepper, sage, thyme, oregano, and coconut oil to it, and blend all the items for 3 minutes. Give some rest to the machine and blend again until it becomes a smooth sauce.

4. When the rice is cooked, remove them from the heat. Serve wild rice with mushroom hemp sauce and enjoy!

Nutritional Content

Calories 238.4kcal | **Carbs** 32.5g | **Protein** 10g | **Fat** 9g | **Fiber** 3.6g

Okra with Artichoke Sauce

Prep Time
11 minutes

Cook Time
3 minutes

Yield
2

What you will need

- **Okra**, 1 cup/5.6oz./160g
- **Artichoke**, 1 /3oz./85g
- **Agave syrup**, 1 tablespoon/0.74fl. oz./21ml
- **Tomatoes**, ¼ cup/1.59oz./45g
- **Onion**, ¼ cup/1.71oz./48.5g

Directions

1. Add artichoke, agave syrup, tomatoes, and onions in the blender and blend all the items, until become smooth.

2. Roast the okra in a pan for 2 minutes and dish it out.

3. Serve the okra with artichoke sauce and enjoy!

Nutritional Content

Calories 83.9kcal | **Carbs** 19.3g | **Protein** 3.5g | **Fat** 0.3g | **Fiber** 4.6g

Chapter-8
Dinner Recipes

Alkaline Chickpea Salad

Prep Time
10 minutes

Cook Time
0 minutes

Yield
4

What you will need

- **Chickpeas**, cooked, 2 cups /454g
- **Alkaline Hemp seed mayo**, 2/3 cup /85g
- **Red onions**, diced, ¼ cup /2 oz. /56.7g
- **Green peppers**, diced, 2 tablespoons /28g
- **½ Nori Sheet**
- **Onion powder**, 2 teaspoon /10g
- **Dill**, 1 teaspoon /5g
- **Sea salt**, ¼ teaspoon /1.25g

Directions

1. Firstly, at 425 °F (220 °C) bake the bell peppers for approximately 29 minutes, till well-cooked. Remove seeds and keep them aside.

2. In the bowl mash chickpeas and Nori sheet till the required texture is achieved.

3. Now include the remaining ingredients and stir them well. Keep it in the refrigerator for 55 minutes and serve.

Nutritional Content

Calories 148kcal | **Crabs** 18.5g | **Protein** 7.85g | **Fat** 2.25g | **Fiber** 6.9g

Ginger Soursop Soup

Prep Time
9 minutes

Cook Time
55 minutes

Yield
3

What you will need

- **Soursop Leaves**, 3
- **Chayote squash**, cubed, 1 cup /8 oz. /227g
- **Spring water**, 6 cups /1500ml
- **Zucchini**, cubed, ½ cup /4 oz. /113.4g
- **Kale**, chopped 1 cup /8 oz. /227g
- **Onions**, diced, ½ cup /4 oz. /113.4g
- **Red peppers**, diced, ½ cup /4 oz. /113.4g
- **Onion powder**, 1.5 tablespoons /21g
- **Green peppers**, diced, ½ cup /4 oz. /113.4g
- **Sea salt**, 2 teaspoons /10g
- **Quinoa**, ½ cup /4 oz. /113.4g
- **Basil**, ½ tablespoon /7g
- **Summer squash**, cubed, ½ cup /4 oz. /113.4g
- **Fresh ginger**, minced, ½ tablespoon /7g
- **Cayenne**, one pinch
- **Oregano**, ½ tablespoon /7g

Directions

1. Firstly, rinse the soursop leaves and cut them in half, and put them in a pan with 2 cups of water.

2. Let it boil for 16 minutes or more while it is covered with a lid. After that required time you can remove the leaves from the water.

3. Now include all the remaining ingredients in it. Include the remaining 4 cups of spring water.

4. Mix the ingredients thoroughly, cover it and cook for 32 to 42 minutes.

5. Pour into a soup bowl and serve warm.

Nutritional Content

Calories 96.6kcal | **Crabs** 12.9g | **Protein** 4.26g | **Fat** 1.7g | **Fiber** 5.5g

Alkaline Cheese Taco

Prep Time
15 minutes

Cook Time
10 minutes

Yield
4

What you will need

FOR MUSHROOM MIXTURE

- **Onions**, sliced, 1 cup /8 oz. /227g
- **Portabella mushroom caps**, 4
- **Red peppers**, diced, 1 cup /8 oz. /227g
- **Onion powder**, 1 tablespoon/14g
- **Thyme**, 1 teaspoon /5g
- **Green peppers**, diced, 1 cup /8 oz. /227g
- **Alkaline garlic sauce**,
  ½ cup /4 oz. /113.4g
- **Sea salt**, 1 teaspoon /5g
- **Grapeseed oil**, 1 tablespoon /15ml
- **Oregano**, 1 teaspoon /5g
- **Savory**, 1 teaspoon /5g

FOR CHEESE

- **Basil**, ½ teaspoon /2.5g
- **Cayenne**, ½ teaspoon /2.5g
- **Oregano**, ½ teaspoon /2.5g
- **Sea salt**, ½ teaspoon /2.5g
- **Onion powder**, 1.5 teaspoons /7.5g
- **Brazil nuts**, soaked,
  ¾ cup /6 oz. /169.8g
- **Spring water**, ½ cup /125ml
- **Hemp seeds**, 1.5 tablespoons /21g

Directions

1. Cut the mushrooms into pieces round 1/8" thick.

2. Take a bowl and in it mix the garlic sauce and seasonings. Now include the mushrooms to it and keep it for 28 minutes.

3. For the preparation of cheese add all the ingredients of cheese in the blender and blend it till it is smooth.

4. On medium heat cook peppers and onions for 5 minutes then include marinated mushrooms in it and cook for 5 minutes more.

5. Place in flatbread and fold it to the shape of a taco and enjoy.

Nutritional Content

Calories 275.75kcal | **Crabs** 12g | **Protein** 7.2g | **Fat** 22g | **Fiber** 4.75g

Alkaline Meatballs

Prep Time
15 minutes

Cook Time
4 minutes

Yield
15

What you will need

- **Onions**, chopped, ½ cup /4 oz. /113.4g
- **Mushroom**, chopped, 1 cup /8 oz. /227g
- **Garbanzo beans**, cooked, ¾ cup /6 oz. /169.8g
- **Green peppers**, chopped, 2 tablespoons /28g
- **Garbanzo bean flour**, ¼ cup /2 oz. /56.7g
- **Onion powder**, ½ tablespoons /7g
- **Sea salt**, ½ teaspoon /2.5g
- **Grapeseed oil**
- **Oregano**, 1 teaspoon /5g
- **Fennel powder**, ½ teaspoon /2.5g
- **Savory**, ½ teaspoon /2.5g
- **Dill**, ½ teaspoon /2.5g
- **Basil**, 1 teaspoon /5g
- **Sage**, ½ teaspoon /2.5g
- **Ginger powder**, one pinch
- **Cayenne powder**, one pinch
- **Cloves**, grounded, one pinch
- **Alkaline tomato sauce**, 3 cups /691g

Directions

1. In the blender blend all the ingredients excluding tomato sauce, flour, and oil.

2. In the bowl add this mixture and add flour in it to give it the shape of balls. Make the meatballs and keep them aside for cooking.

3. Grease the skillet with grapeseed oil and place meatballs in it cook and flip them with help of tongs and make sure to cook them from all sides, for about 3 to 4 minutes.

4. Now add them to a tomato sauce and let it simmer for 4 minutes.

5. Serve with either cooked wild rice or flatbread.

Nutritional Content

Calories 35.9kcal | **Crabs** 3.37g | **Protein** 1.54g | **Fat** 1.26g | **Fiber** 1.6

Alkaline Mushroom Stew

Prep Time
15 minutes

Cook Time
3 Hours

Yield
6

What you will need

- **White Onions**, chopped, 1 cup /8 oz. /227g

- **Portabella mushroom**, chopped, 2 cups

- **Red onions**, chopped, ½ cup

- **Garbanzo beans**, cooked, 1 cup

- **Kale**, chopped, 1 cup

- **Red peppers**, diced, ½ cup /4 oz. /113.4g

- **Butternut squash**, chopped, ½ cup /4 oz. /113.4g

- **Onion powder**, 2 tablespoons /28g

- **Plum tomatoes**, chopped, 2

- **Green peppers**, diced, ½ cup /4 oz. /113.4g

- **Alkaline garlic sauce**, ½ cup /4 oz. /113.4g

- **Sea salt**, 2 teaspoons /10g

- **Grapeseed oil**, 2 tablespoons /30ml

- **Oregano**, 1 teaspoon /5g

- **Thyme**, ½ teaspoon /2.5g

- **Savory**, 1 teaspoon /5g

- **Basil**, 1 teaspoon /5g

- **Sage**, ½ teaspoon /2.5g

- **Ginger powder**, ½ teaspoon /2.5g

- **Spring water**, 4 cups /125ml

Directions

1. Include the complete ingredients and seasonings in the slow cooker and stir it.

2. Let it cook it for 3 hours on high heat, while mixing it after every hour.

3. Pour into the bowl and serve warm.

Nutritional Content

Calories 189.65kcal | **Crabs** 22g | **Protein** 8g | **Fat** 5.375g | **Fiber** 8.6g

Chickpea Burger

What you will need

- **Onions**, chopped, ¼ cup /2 oz. /56.7g
- **Garbanzo bean flour**, ½ cup /4 oz. /113.4g
- **Green peppers**, diced, ¼ cup/2 oz. /56.7g
- **Kale**, diced, ¼ cup, /2 oz. /56.7g
- **½ Plum tomato**, diced
- **Basil**, 1 teaspoon /5g
- **Oregano**, 1 teaspoon /5g
- **Sea Salt**, 1 teaspoon /5g
- **Dill**, ½ teaspoon /2.5g
- **Ginger powder**, one pinch
- **Onion powder**, 1 teaspoon /5g
- **Cayenne powder**, one pinch
- **Spring water**, ¼ cup /59ml
- **Grape seed Oil**

Directions

Prep Time	Cook Time	Yield
9 minutes	5 minutes	2

1. In the blender blend all the ingredients except tomato sauce, flour and oil. Mix all the vegetables and seasonings in the bowl, then include flour in it.

2. Now add water slowly in it till this mixture can be formed into a patty. You can add more flour if it is runny.

3. Now heat the oil on the skillet and cook patties for 3 minutes each of its side, till it is brown. Now cut the flatbread into a circle shape and place a patty in it you can add lettuce leaf or tomato if you war and serve.

Nutritional Content

Calories 199kcal | **Crabs** 14g | **Protein** 8.15g | **Fat** 8g | **Fiber** 9.85g

Alkaline Alfredo Pasta

What you will need

- **Spelt Tortellini pasta**, 10 oz. /283g
- **White onions**, diced, ½ cup /4 oz. /113.4g
- **Summer squash**, 1
- **Mushrooms**, ½ cup /4 oz. /113.4g
- **Zucchini squash**, 1
- **Green peppers**, diced, ½ cup /4 oz. /113.4g
- **Red peppers**, diced, ½ cup /4 oz. /113.4g
- **Basil**, 1 teaspoon /5g
- **Sea salt**, 2 teaspoon /10g
- **Onion powder**, 2 teaspoon /10g
- **Grapeseed Oil**
- **Cayenne Powder**, one pinch
    - **Oregano**, 1 teaspoon /5g
    - **Brazil nut cheese**, ¼ cup / 2oz. /56.7g

Directions

Prep Time	Cook Time	Yield
5 minutes	10 minutes	4

1. Firstly, boil the pasta and then drain and keep it aside.

2. Heat the oil in the skillet and include vegetables and seasonings ir it and cook them for 3 minutes.

3. Now add pasta and cheese to it.

4. Mix it and cook for one minute more. Serve warm.

Nutritional Content

Calories 278kcal | **Crabs** 54g | **Protein** 10.55g | **Fat** 1.47g | **Fiber** 3.975g

Fried Wild Rice

What you will need

- **Wild rice (soaked overnight)**, 1 cup /8 oz. /227g
- **Butternut squash**, diced, ¼ cup /2 oz. /56.7g
- **Spring water**, 4 cups /1000ml
- **White onions**, diced, ¼ cup /2 oz. /56.7g
- **Fresh ginger**, minced, 1 teaspoon /5g
- **Red & green peppers**, diced, ¼ cup /2 oz. /56.7g
- **Basil**, ½ teaspoon /2.5g
- **Green onions**, diced, ¼ cup /2 oz. /56.7g
- **Sea salt**, ½ teaspoon /2.5g
- **Crushed red pepper**, one pinch
- **Onion powder**, ½ teaspoon /2.5g
- **Grapeseed Oil**

Prep Time	Cook Time	Yield
9 minutes	1h, 10 minutes	2

Directions

1. In the pot add rice and water, cover it and let it boil. When it started to boil lower the heat and let it cook for 1 hour and mix every 10 minutes or till all the water is evaporated.

2. Heat 1 tablespoon grapeseed oil in a skillet and cook vegetables and seasonings for 4 minutes.

3. Now include rice into the skillet and cook for 5 minutes more.

4. Place in bowl or plate and enjoy!

Nutritional Content

Calories 129.9kcal | **Crabs** 21g | **Protein** 4g | **Fat** 2.65g | **Fiber** 3g

Alkaline Cheese Macaroni

Prep Time	Cook Time	Yield
6 minutes	38 minutes	8

What you will need

- **Kamut Spirals**, 1 box, 12 oz. 339.6g
- **Brazil Nuts (soaked overnight)**, ½ lb. /227g
- **Garbanzo Bean Flour**, ¼ cup /2 oz. /56.7g
- **Spring Water**, 1 cup /250ml
- **Grapeseed Oil**, 2 teaspoon /10g
- **Onion Powder**, 2 teaspoon /10g
- **Sea Salt**, 1 teaspoon /5g
- **Ground Annatto**, ½ teaspoon /2.5g
- **Juice of ½ lime**
- **Hemp Milk**, 1 cup /250ml

Directions

1. In the pot add rice and water, cover it and let it boil. When it started to boil lower the heat

2. Firstly, boil the pasta according to the instructions.

3. Heat the oven before to 350 °F (180 °C) for the preparation of Brazil nut sauce include all the ingredients in the processor and blend it till smooth.

4. Put pasta in a greased baking dish and transfer all the sauce above the top and mix it.

5. Cook it for 25 minutes. Serve and enjoy!

Nutritional Content

Calories 351.5kcal | **Crabs** 24.3g | **Protein** 12g | **Fat** 22g | **Fiber** 7.4g

Quinoa with Kale and Mushroom

Prep Time
10 minutes

Cook Time
21 minutes

Yield
3

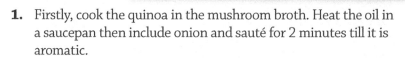

What you will need

- **Quinoa**, 1 cup /8 oz. /227g
- **Grapeseed oil**, 2 tablespoons /30ml
- **Spring water**, ¼ cup /59ml
- **1 small white onion**, diced
- **Mushroom broth**, 2 cups /500ml
- **Cremini mushrooms**, sliced, 2 cups /454g
- **Sea salt**, to taste
- **Onion powder**, 1 teaspoon /5g
- **Curly kale**, 3 cups /681g
- **Thyme**, 2 tablespoons /28g
- **Juice of 1 lemon**
- **Oregano**, 2 tablespoon /28g

Directions

1. Firstly, cook the quinoa in the mushroom broth. Heat the oil in a saucepan then include onion and sauté for 2 minutes till it is aromatic.

2. Include mushrooms in it and cook for 2 minutes, till they start to tender. Now include kale in it and salt, onion powder, thyme, and oregano, and mix it thoroughly. Let it cook for 3 minutes till the ka starts to wilt.

3. Add the spring water and lemon juice to it. Cook for a few minutes, till the liquid, is reduced. Continue stirring while cooking.

4. Once it is done mix quinoa with vegetables and mix them. Enjoy!

Nutritional Content

Calories 262.6kcal | **Crabs** 22g | **Protein** 9.66g | **Fat** 12.7g | **Fiber** 11g

Quick Creamy Pasta

Prep Time
9 minutes

Cook Time
21 minutes

Yield
4

What you will need

- **Spelt pasta**, 8 oz. /224g
- **Tahini butter**, 3 tablespoons /42g
- **Cremini mushrooms**, thinly sliced, 1 ½ lb. /681g
- **White onions**, diced, 1 cup /8 oz. /227g
- **Sea salt**, one pinch
- **Fresh thyme**, chopped, 4 teaspoons /20g
- **Garbanzo bean flour**, 2 ½ tablespoons /35g
- **Spring water**, 2 cups /500ml
- **Cayenne**, grounded, 1 ½ teaspoons /7.5g
  - **Brazil nut cheese**, ¾ cup /6 oz. /168g
  - **Fresh sweet basil**, chopped, 2 tablespoons /28g

Directions

1. Cook pasta in boiling water permitting to the instructions on the package.

2. In the skillet melt the butter, include onions and mushrooms in i and mix it and cook till brown, for 6 minutes, sprinkle salt, cayen thyme, and cook till aromatic, for about one minute.

3. Now mix in the flour and heat for 1 minute. Now gradually inclu spring water to it while mixing. Let it boil then reduce the heat ar cook for 5 minutes till it gets thick.

4. Include pasta and Brazil nut cheese in it, and cook for 3 minutes. Sprinkle sweet basil on top and serve.

Nutritional Content

Calories 378kcal | **Crabs** 52gg | **Protein** 16g | **Fat** 8.95g | **Fiber** 9.5g

Vegetable Fajita

Prep Time
6 minutes

Cook Time
6minutes

Yield
6

What you will need

- **Mushrooms**, sliced, 3 cups /681g
- **White onions**, diced, 1 ½ cup /340g
- **Green and red bell pepper**, diced, 1 ½ cup /340g
- **Sea salt**, 2 teaspoons /10g
- **Oregano**, 2 teaspoon /10g
- **Cayenne**, ½ teaspoon /2.5g
- **Onion powder**, 2 teaspoons /10g
- **Sweet basil**, 2 teaspoon /10g
- **Juice of ½ lime**
- **Grapeseed oil**, 1 tablespoon /15ml

Directions

1. In a skillet add grapeseed oil and heat it.

2. Now add vegetables and seasoning and cook them for about 6 minutes.

3. Once it is done serve warm over spelt tortillas.

Nutritional Content

Calories 78.6kcal | **Crabs** 9.6g | **Protein** 2.83g | **Fat** 2.8g | **Fiber** 3.16g

Kamut Patties

Prep Time
6 minutes

Cook Time
5 minutes

Yield
12 patties

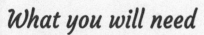

What you will need

- **Red onions**, diced, 1 cup /340g
- **Kamut cereal**, cooked, 3 cups /681g
- **Green and yellow bell pepper**, diced, 1 cup /340g
- **Sea salt**, 1 teaspoon /5g
- **Spelt flour**, 1 cup /8 oz. /227g
- **Oregano**, 1 tablespoon /14g
- **Grapeseed oil**, 1 tablespoon
- **Cayenne**, ½ teaspoon /2.5g
- **Onion powder**, 1 tablespoon /14g
- **Hemp milk**, ½ cup /125ml
- **Sweet basil**, 1 tablespoon /14g

Directions

1. Combine the vegetables, milk and Kamut, and seasonings in one bowl.

2. Now include ½ cup flour and mix till this mixture can be formed into the patty.

3. Shape it into 12 patties. Heat the oil on a skillet and cook patties for 5 minutes on each side, till it is brown.

4. Serve with alkaline ketchup and enjoy!

Nutritional Content(patty)

Calories 114.6kcal | **Crabs** 18.15g | **Protein** 4.3g | **Fat** 2.0g | **Fiber** 3.4g

Alkaline Chili Stew

What you will need

- **10 Roma plum tomatoes**, diced
- **1 Tomatillo**, diced
- **Onions**, diced, ½ cup /4 oz. /113g
- **Garbanzo Beans**, Cooked, 3 cups /681g
- **Green bell pepper**, diced, ½ cup /4 oz. /113g
- **Spring water**, 1 cup /250ml
- **Red bell pepper**, diced, ½ cup /4 oz. /113g
- **Sea salt**, 2 teaspoons /10g
- **Oregano**, 1 teaspoon /5g
- **Cayenne**, 1 teaspoon /5g
- **Onion powder**, 2 teaspoons /10g
- **Sweet basil**, 1 teaspoon /5g
- **Grapeseed oil**, 2 teaspoons /10g
- **Annatto**, ½ teaspoon /5g

Prep Time	Cook Time	Yield
14 minutes	1hour , 7minutes	6

Directions

1. In a pot add grapeseed oil and heat it.

2. Now sauté tomatillo, bell peppers, and onions for 4 to 5 minutes. Include tomatoes, beans, and spring water in it sprinkle all seasonings and mix it well. Let it cook for 1 hour on low heat.

3. Once it is done serve warm with rice or flatbread.

Nutritional Content

Calories 193kcal | **Crabs** 23.6g | **Protein** 9.16g | **Fat** 4.08g | **Fiber** 8.86

Falafel

Prep Time	Cook Time	Yield
10 minutes	20 minutes	6

What you will need

- **Hemp seed hearts**, 5 tablespoons /140g
- **Sea salt**, 1 teaspoon /5g
- **Garbanzo beans**, cooked, 1 cup /8 oz. /227g
- **Onion**, minced, ½ small
- **Cayenne pepper**, 1 teaspoon /5g
- **Thyme**, basil, savory, grounded, 1 cup /227g

Directions

1. Warm the oven to 450 °F (230 °C) and arrange the parchment pap on a baking pan.

2. Add chickpeas, and herbs in blend them till they turned into grain and break down well.

3. Transfer it to a bowl and include hemp seed hearts, salt, cayenne pepper, and onion in it.

4. Make falafel and bake them for 20 minutes till brown. Serves with tahini butter.

Nutritional Content

Calories 189kcal | **Crabs** 6.7g | **Protein** 10.6g | **Fat** 11g | **Fiber** 6g

Stuffed Bell Peppers

Prep Time
10 minutes

Cook Time
20 minutes

Yield
4-6

What you will need

- **4-6 Bell Peppers**
- **Mushrooms**, sliced, ½ lb. /227g
- **Cayenne Powder**, ½ teaspoon /2.5g
- **2 Plum tomatoes**, diced
- **Onion Powder**, 1 teaspoon /5g
- **Wild rice**, cooked, 2 cups /454g
- **½ White onion**, chopped
- **Sea salt**, 1 teaspoon /5g
- **Tomato sauce**, 1 cup /8 oz. /227g
- **Brazil nut cheese**, 1 ½ cup /340g
- **½ Red onion**, chopped
- **Grapeseed oil**, 2 tablespoons/30ml
- **Oregano**, 1 teaspoon /5g

Directions

1. For the peppers cut off the pepper's top and remove the seeds.

2. Place them in hot water so that they soften. Then remove from it and place it on a baking sheet, sprinkling sea salt.

3. For the preparation of vegetables, Sauté mushrooms, onions, and seasoning in grapeseed oil for 5 minutes.

4. Now add tomatoes, wild rice, alkaline tomato sauce, and Brazil nut cheese about 1 cup, and cook for 4 to 5 minutes.

5. Now stuff the peppers with this mixture and the remaining tomato sauce and Brazil nut cheese.

6. Bake it in the oven at 350 °F (180 °C) for 30 minutes. Serve.

Nutritional Content

Calories 193kcal | **Crabs** 23.6g | **Protein** 9.16g | **Fat** 4.08g | **Fiber** 8.86g

Tangy Arugula Pasta

Prep Time
10 minutes

Cook Time
20 minutes

Yield
4-6

What you will need

- **Hemp seed hearts**, 1 ½ cups /340g
- **Spelt pasta**, 12 oz. /336g
- **Juice of 2 limes**
- **Spring water**, ½ cup /4 oz. /113.4g
- **Sea salt**, ½ teaspoon /2.5g
- **Cherry tomatoes**, 1 cup /8 oz. /227g
- **Basil leaves**, 1 cup /8 oz. /227g
- **Arugula**, 2 cups /454g

Directions

1. Cook pasta according to the instructions on the package.

2. To make the sauce, mix hemp seed hearts, lime juice, ½ cup water, salt, and basil leaves in a blender and blend it.

3. Strain the pasta and add it to the pot and add the sauce in it, mix to coat it properly. Now include arugula, and cherry tomatoes and mix again. It is ready to serve.

Nutritional Content

Calories 797.5kcal | **Crabs** 62g | **Protein** 39.5g | **Fat** 38g | **Fiber** 12.45g

Alkaline Sloppy Garbanzo Beans

Prep Time
6 minutes

Cook Time
10 minutes

Yield
6

What you will need

- **Onions**, diced, ½ cup /4 oz. /113.4g
- **Spelt**, cooked, 2 cups /454g
- **Garbanzo beans**, cooked, 1 cup /8 oz. /227f
- **Green bell pepper**, diced, ½ cup /4 oz. /113.4g
- **Sea salt**, 1 teaspoon /5g
- **Oregano**, 1 tablespoon /14g
- **Grapeseed oil**, 1 tablespoon/15ml
- **Cayenne**, one pinch
- **Onion powder**, 1 teaspoon /5g
- **Alkaline barbecue sauce**, 1 ½ cup /340g

Directions

1. Add garbanzo beans and spelt in a blender and blend for 15 seconds till smooth.

2. Warm the oil in a skillet and sauté the peppers, onions, and seasonings for 4 minutes.

3. Now stir in the blended ingredients and barbecue sauce and cook for 5 minutes.

4. Serve with flatbread.

Nutritional Content

Calories 159kcal | **Crabs** 22g | **Protein** 6.3g | **Fat** 3.6g | **Fiber** 5g

Grilled Zucchini Wraps

Prep Time
11 minutes

Cook Time
7 minutes

Yield
2

What you will need

- **Red onions**, sliced, 2 tablespoons /28g
- **1 Zucchini**, sliced
- **Sea salt**, to taste
- **Cayenne powder**, one pinch
- **Grapeseed oil**, 1 tablespoon /15ml
- **Cherry tomatoes**, ½ cup /4 oz. /113.4g
- **Kale stems removed**, 1 cup
- **Brazil nut cheese**, ¼ cup /2 oz. /56.7g
- **2 large spelt tortillas**
  - **Hummus**, 4 tablespoons /56g

Directions

1. Place sliced zucchini in a bowl, include oil, salt, and cayenne in it and mix well.

2. Cook it directly on the grill for 3 minutes flip it and cook for 2 minutes more. Keep it aside.

3. Warm the tortillas on the grill. To assemble the wraps, spread 2 tablespoons of hummus and 2 tablespoons of Brazil nut cheese on each tortilla, add zucchini slices, ½ cup of kale on each tortilla, and tomato. Wrap it and enjoy!

Nutritional Content

Calories 291kcal | **Crabs** 32.35g | **Protein** 7.95g | **Fat** 13.5g | **Fiber** 4.65g

Mushroom Chayote Soup

Prep Time
10 minutes

Cook Time
35 minutes

Yield
6/8

What you will need

- **Onions**, diced, 1 cup /8 oz. /227g
- **Garbanzo beans flour**, 1 ½ cup /340g
- **Mushrooms**, sliced, 3 cups /681g
- **Vegetable broth**, 1 cup
- **Hemp milk**, 1 cup
- **Chayote squash**, diced, 2 cups /4 oz. /113.4g
- **Spring water**, 6 cups
- **Sea salt**, 2 teaspoon /10g
- **Grapeseed oil**, 1 tablespoon/15ml
- **Basil**, 2 teaspoon /10g
- **Onion powder**, 1 tablespoon /14g
- **Crushed red pepper**, 1 teaspoon /5g

Directions

1. Add garbanzo beans and spelt in the blender and blend for 15 seconds till smooth.

2. Cut the chayote squash into cubes after removing its skin.

3. Sauté onions and mushrooms in grape seed oil for 3 minutes. Add 4 cups spring water, milk, vegetable broth, chayote, and seasoning in a pot and stir it.

4. Take 2 cups of water and garbanzo bean flour in a blender and blend for 20 seconds till there is no lump.

5. Add this mixture to a pot and cook for 31 minutes, mixing occasionally. Remove from heat after the required time and serve.

Nutritional Content

Calories 193.8kcal | **Crabs** 17g | **Protein** 9.9g | **Fat** 5g | **Fiber** 12g

Vegetable Hemp Nuggets

Prep Time
8 minutes

Cook Time
30 minutes

Yield
6

What you will need

- **Lettuce**, ½ bunch
- **Quinoa**, cooked, 1 cup /8 oz. /227g
- **3 Zucchini**, grated
- **Sea salt**, one big pinch
- **Thyme**, sage, basil, ¼ cup /2 oz. /56.7g
- **Hemp seeds**, 1/3 cup
- **Cayenne powder**, 1 teaspoon /5g
- **Grapeseed oil**, 1 tablespoon /15ml

Directions

1. Warm the oven before to 425 °F (220 °C). Arrange the parchment paper in a baking tray.

2. Sauté greens and zucchini in grapeseed oil. Sprinkle cayenne pepper and sea salt. Remove from heat and let it cool. Then add it to the blender. Include quinoa, hemp seeds, and herbs and blend them till it clumps together.

3. Form the nuggets with your hands and place them in a baking tray brush with oil lightly.

4. Cook in the oven for 30 minutes, changing sides halfway through. Once done serve with sauce of your own choice.

Nutritional Content(patty)

Calories 128kcal | **Crabs** 8.6g | **Protein** 5.6g | **Fat** 7.6g | **Fiber** 2.58g

Anti-inflammatory Vegetable Blend

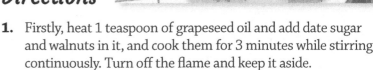

Prep Time
11 minutes

Cook Time
37 minutes

Yield
4

What you will need

- **Grapeseed oil**, 2 teaspoon /10ml
- **Homemade vegetable broth**, 4 cups /1000ml
- **Quinoa**, cooked, 2 cups /454g
- **Fresh basil**, 1 teaspoon /5g
- **Butternut squash**, diced, 1 large
- **Watercress**, chopped, 4 cups /908g
- **Walnuts**, ½ cup /4 oz. /113.4g
- **Date sugar**, 1 tablespoon /14g

Directions

1. Firstly, heat 1 teaspoon of grapeseed oil and add date sugar and walnuts in it, and cook them for 3 minutes while stirring continuously. Turn off the flame and keep it aside.

2. Heat remaining oil in the same skillet and cook butternut squash fo 5 minutes, till it is brown. Now add homemade vegetable broth and basil and bring it to a boil then reduce the heat and cook for 18 to 20 minutes, till squash is soft. You can include more broth if needed.

3. Once it is done now include chopped watercress and cook for 3 minutes more or till it is wilted.

4. Take it away from the heat and add already cooked quinoa. Mix to combine and sprinkle walnuts and serve.

Nutritional Content

Calories 320kcal | **Crabs** 38g | **Protein** 10g | **Fat** 11g | **Fiber** 9.5g

Vegan Pizza Boats

Prep Time
15 minutes

Cook Time
20 minutes

Yield
4

What you will need

- **Grapeseed oil**, 1 teaspoon /5ml
- **4 zucchinis**, sliced in half lengthwise
- **Mushrooms**, sliced, ½ cup /4 oz. /113.4g
- **Alkaline pizza sauce**, ½ cup /4 oz. /113.4g
- **1 small red onion**, diced
- **Green pepper**, diced, ½ cup /4 oz. /113.4g
- **Sesame tahini butter**, 1 cup /8 oz. /227g
- **Fresh basil**, chopped, 1 tablespoon /14g

Directions

1. Sauté mushrooms and bell peppers, and onions in grapeseed oil ar keep them aside.

2. Heat the oven before to 400 °F (200 °C). Cut the zucchini in half lengthwise. Take out the pulp. Spread alkaline pizza sauce on each half, then add onions, bell peppers, and tomatoes equally on each half.

3. Now top with sesame tahini butter and sprinkle basil on the top. Place in the long baking dish and cook for 15 minutes.

4. Serve warm.

Nutritional Content

Calories 375kcal | **Crabs** 15g | **Protein** 12.7g | **Fat** 29g | **Fiber** 7.7g

Zucchini Noodles with Green Sauce

Prep Time
19 minutes

Cook Time
21 minutes

Yield
4

What you will need

- **Grapeseed oil**, 1 teaspoon /5ml
- **Yellow onion**, chopped, ½ small
- **Thyme**, 1 teaspoon /5g
- **Fresh basil leaves**, 2 cups /454g
- **Green pumpkin seeds**, toasted, ½ cup /4 oz. /113.4g
- **Olive oil**, ⅓ cup /79ml
- **Lemon juice**, 2 teaspoons /10ml
- **Pinch of red pepper flakes**
- **Sea salt**, to taste
- **3 large zucchinis**
- **Fresh basil leaves**, for garnishing

Directions

1. For the preparation of green sauce. Add onion, basil, thyme, pumpkin seeds, olive oil, and lemon juice in a blender. Blend it till it has a smooth consistency. Sprinkle salt to your taste.

2. For the preparation of noodles. Turn the zucchini into noodles with a julienne peeler or with a spiralizer. You can either grate it a long way on a large grater.

3. Add sauce to the noodles and mix till coated well. Sprinkle salt.

4. Transfer it to a large plate and sprinkle it with fresh basil.

Nutritional Content

Calories 221kcal | **Crabs** 11g | **Protein** 2.8g | **Fat** 19.7g | **Fiber** 4g

Roasted Red Pepper Curry

Prep Time
10 minutes

Cook Time
55 minutes

Yield
6

What you will need

- **Grapeseed oil**, 1 teaspoon /5ml
- **Red bell peppers**, 14 oz. /392g
- **Grapeseed oil**, 3 tablespoons/45ml
- **1 red onion**, diced
- **Cloves**, 1 teaspoon /5g
- **Sea salt**, one pinch
- **Cayenne pepper**, one pinch
- **Coconut milk**, 1 1/3 cups / 333ml
- **Spelt flour**, 2 ½ tablespoons /42g
- **Onion powder**, 1 teaspoon /5g
- **Garbanzo beans**, 1 ¼ cups /283.7g
- **Kale**, 1 cup /8 oz. /227g
- **Cherry tomatoes**, ¾ cup /168g

Directions

1. Firstly, at 425 °F (220 °C) bake the bell peppers for approximately 29 minutes, till well-cooked. Remove seeds and keep them aside.

2. Sauté onion and cloves in oil in the meantime bell peppers are roasting. Sprinkle salt and pepper and keep it aside too.

3. Combine onion, cloves, peppers, coconut milk, spelt flour, and onion powder in the blender and blend it till combined well.

4. Put it in the skillet, including chickpeas and kale, and tomato halves, and cook in the oven again at 390 °F (198 °C) for 30 minutes. it is ready to serve after a certain time you can serve it with flatbread or wild rice.

Nutritional Content

Calories 243kcal | **Crabs** 29.5g | **Protein** 6.3g | **Fat** 11g | **Fiber** 5g

Conclusion

The Dr. Sebi diet is an easy manageable dietary regime that can help you lose weight, improv heart health and prevent low immunity and inflammation.

I have specially crafted meal pans for you. A 7-day detox meal plan. This will help you to sta this diet and cleanse your body of harmful toxins. After rejuvenating the body, A 30-day meal pla to help you incorporate this diet into your daily life. All essentials that you will need to start th diet are mentioned in the grocery list. So that the next time you go shopping for your groceries yo will just need to grab the Dr. Sebi diet shopping list and easily plan your meals ahead of time. A working mums can relax because everything from snacks to dinner and breakfast will be planne No more fuss over meal prep!

There are 160 recipes in this book ranging from breakfasts, side dishes, and even sandwiche If you are wondering whether you can enjoy your favorite pasta on this diet. Yes! you can. N only this you will also have a wide assortment of juices to enjoy. Every ingredient in the recipes alkaline, plant-based, and of high nutritional value. They not only taste great but they also ha cleansing and detoxing properties that will rid your body of toxins. Every recipe has its nutrition value mentioned next to it so you can easily track your calories. In your weight loss journey.

Lastly, the journey from a meat-eating diet to a plant-based Dr. Sebi diet may appear dauntir and at times out of reach. But with consistency and with the guidance in this book you can do You have all the tools you will need to make a change. You just need to believe in yourself that yo can do it. This is not possible without love. The love for nature and most importantly the love fo your body.

Conversation
Charts

VOLUME EQUIVALENTS (Liquid)

Us standard	Us standard Ounces	Metric Approximate
2 tbsp.	1 fl. oz.	30 mL
¼ cup	2 fl. oz.	60 mL
½ cup	4 fl. oz.	120 mL
1 cup	8 fl. oz.	240 mL
1½ cups	12 fl. oz.	355 mL
2 cups or 1 pint	16 fl. oz.	475 mL
4 cups or 1 quart	32 fl. oz.	1 L
1 gallon	128 fl. oz.	4 L

OVEN TEMPERATURE

Fahrenheit (f) (approximate)	Celsius (c) (approximate)
250°F	120°C
300°F	150°C
325°F	165°C
350°F	180°C
375°F	190°C
400°F	200°C
425°F	220°C
450°F	230°C

VOLUME EQUIVALENTS (Dry)

Us standard (approximate)	Metric (approximate)
1/8 tsp.	0.5 mL
¼ tsp.	1 mL
½ tsp.	2 mL
¾ tsp.	4 mL
1 tsp.	5 mL
1 tbsp.	15 mL
¼ cup	59 mL
1/3 cup	79 mL
½ cup	118 mL
2/3 cup	156 mL
¾ cup	177 mL
1 cup	235 mL
2 cups or 1 pint	475 mL
3 cups	700 mL
4 cups or 1 quart	1 L

WEIGHT EQUIVALENTS

Us standard (approximate)	Metric (approximate)
½ ounce	15 g
1 ounce	30 g
2 ounces	60 g
4 ounces	115 g
8 ounces	225 g
12 ounces	340 g
16 ounces or 1 pound	455 g

Index

Made in the USA
Coppell, TX
22 November 2022